TRADOC Historical Monograph Series

SLAM
The Influence of S.L.A. Marshall on the United States Army

by
Major F.D.G. Williams

edited and introduced
by
Susan Canedy

Office of the Command Historian
United States Army Training and Doctrine Command
Fort Monroe, Virginia
and
Center of Military History
United States Army
Washington, D.C., 1994

Library of Congress Cataloging-in-Publication Data

Williams, F.D.G. (Frederick Deane Goodwin), 1953–
    SLAM: the influence of S.L.A. Marshall on the United States Army
  / by F.D.G. Williams ;   edited and introduced by Susan Canedy.
        p.   cm. — (TRADOC historical monograph series)
    Includes bibliographical references (p.   ).
    1. United States.   Army—History—20th century.   2. Marshall, S.
L.A. (Samuel Lyman Atwood), 1900–1977.   3. Military art and
science—United States—History—20th century.   I. Canedy, Susan.
II. Title.   III. Series.
UA25.W55   1990
355′.00973—dc20   90–6739
                                                                    CIP

First Printed 1990—CMH Pub 70–64

U.S. ARMY TRAINING AND DOCTRINE COMMAND

General Frederick M. Franks, Jr.	Commander
Major General John P. Herrling	Chief of Staff
Dr. James T. Stensvaag	Acting Command Historian
Mr. John L. Romjue	Chief, Historical Research and Publication

TRADOC HISTORICAL MONOGRAPH SERIES
Henry O. Malone and John L. Romjue, General Editors

TRADOC Historical Monographs are published by the Office of the Command Historian, U.S. Army Training and Doctrine Command. These studies of training and leader development, and doctrinal and combat developments subjects, provide historical perspective to support the Command's mission of preparing the Army for war and charting its future.

FOREWORD

When a young, serving officer in the United States Army takes on the task of analyzing the complex personality of a man like S.L.A. Marshall, and then attempts to discover and assign measures of value to the contributions made by this man to the United States Army, his task is formidable. That is what Major Williams has set out to do. But Marshall himself, in the four American wars he attended and committed to record, saw his mission in simple terms: the soldier sent by the nation to stand in battle, to live or to die, has a right to be memorialized.

The reader who follows the exposition of Marshall's contributions probably will wonder what is the exact professional classification for this man. He earned his daily bread as an old-line newspaperman. He testified before the Court at the Hague as a military critic of international renown. The editors who sent him to Spain, the Middle East, and Korea certified that he was a war correspondent. He billed himself in Vietnam as an operations analyst. Toward the end of his life, academic and clinical psychologists claimed him as one of their own. For many years Marshall showed strong resentment when introduced as a "military historian" and when he returned to the General Staff in 1948, beginning long terms of reserve duty, he finessed the whole business by defining his role as "a military critic within the Services." Finally, only a year before he died, Marshall had to admit that he considered himself a field historian.

Actually, Marshall's books and periodical pieces come readily under the classic definition of history, i.e. the story. Read any of Marshall's battle pieces. They resolve into the simple tale deriving from the unfolding and exposition of events as these are experienced by and viewed through the eyes of men at the primal level of combat.

Williams identifies Marshall's contributions to the American soldier, the Army and the nation, as an array of the whole which is rich in practical value, varied in scope and both simple and complex in nature. In private conversations, however, Marshall was very clear as to his most important claim to recognition. He was, in his mind and heart, the author and originator of the interrogation technique generally styled as the unit interview after combat. This device he dated from a Japanese night attack on Makin Island.

Here, for the first time, Marshall gathered and interviewed, as a group, the American survivors and recorded the story as an anonymous third person. Williams carefully documents Marshall's later explanations of his method as this took formal shape and gained Army acceptance and then rejection. To the end of his working days, however, Sam never felt that he had been appropriately and officially credited with this, his major contribution to the study of war.

There was always a background theme in Marshall's attempts, via his interview techniques, to determine the truth obscured by the smoke of battle. This was his devotion to and respect for the American soldier who goes in harm's way. Marshall authored one of the best stories of military disaster ever written, the retreat of the 2d Division—the longest in our history—in the aftermath of the November fight on the Chongchon River during the Korean war. At the close of the tale, Marshall gives no weighing of praise or blame, merely noting that on Christmas Day, the 2d Division "again was a going concern." In the long span of time since Korea, most have forgotten the vilification by the American people and press of the American soldier during the "bug-out" days. Sam never wavered in stalwart defense of the American soldier and won the rather grudging admiration of E. J. Kahn, in the *New Yorker,* who titled him "spokesman for the rabbits."

Now that Marshall is not able to defend the accuracy of his recorded observations of battle, a few have suggested—for the most part with no scrutiny of his notebooks or personal records—that his reportage of battle is not to be trusted. In this book, Williams has done a first class job of analyzing the correlation or lack thereof between the raw data in Marshall's notepads and the final edited text published under his name.

Sam was an honest reporter of the old school—a genius too cynical to bother with selling some agreed-upon tale to the reader. It is true that this breed were aware of the prescription "to point a moral and adorn a tale" as part of their job. When I weighed Sam's Bastogne interviews against the written evidence and other oral testimony developed when I wrote the official Army history of the Battle of the Bulge, they squared with the weight and conformation of all other testimony.

The much debated figure for those firing their weapons in battle, which Marshall set at only 15-25 percent, falls under the same rubric; pointing a moral. Williams has understood what Marshall was trying to do, make the reader (citizen or soldier) understand that the infantry in the rifle line carry the battle and that the nation must provide the training, the motivation, the discipline, the leadership, and, indeed, the culture, to nourish that firing line and recognize "the need in battle for more and better fire." This much debated statistic appeared in *Men Against Fire,* a highly praised essay, but those who wish to truly comprehend Marshall's purpose will find it set forth in another place, *The Soldier's Load and the Mobility of a Nation,* now too often gathering dust in Army libraries alongside old tomes on uniforms and equipment.

Sam belonged to that ancient tribe of storytellers but he also possessed the intuitive perception—honed by professional expertise—to discern such things as the psychophysical bond between fear and fatigue. Williams explains this aspect of Marshall's career with understanding. Sam refused to accept modern science, its gimmicks and promises of a bigger bang for the buck as a guarantee of victory in battle and surety for the survival of the nation.

Williams has a good understanding of the physical and mental attributes which made Marshall's contributions possible and which attracted so many friends and disciples—and, after death, so many enemies. Some saw Sam as pompous and vain. I remember Sam as Kipling described the veteran army mule in *The Jungle Book,* advancing "with the swaggering stomp of an old campaigner."

The author of this book has been singularly successful in accomplishing the task to which he set his hand. Sam, who always gave credit to others for a good job, would, I think, say to Williams, "Well done!" But above all, I am certain that Sam would wish his books to be read as partial tribute to those who "(as) the bravest, meet death with their deeds known only to heaven."

Hugh M. Cole

PREFACE TO THE 1994 EDITION

As this book entered its final stages in 1988–89, Marshall's works again became embroiled in public controversy over his credentials, credibility, and observations. Unfortunately, at that time I could not change the content of the manuscript to address those criticisms without severely delaying the original publication date.

The controversy remains unresolved. Emotions, vested interests, and missing documents all play a part in what is written and discussed. Will the truth ever be known? I cannot say, but I am certain that much more work needs to be done before many important questions can be laid to rest. Certainly what has been written in the past few years is not the final word.

The only factual error in this book that has come to my attention regards a footnote in the last chapter, in which I say that the Army's 44th Military History Detachment does not perform group interviews. I have learned from a modern-day combat historian that the person who gave me that information was mistaken.

Interestingly enough, the combat historians who deployed to the Gulf War of 1990–91 were issued copies of this book. Several have told me that they appreciated the material that described the efforts of the combat historians of World War II. Needless to say, that comment means a great deal to me as a soldier, writer, and historian.

I hope that as other researchers study Marshall and his contributions, they will bring the pendulum back to the center, where it belongs. He was not perfect and gave ammunition to his critics, but his influence on the Army has been both real and beneficial.

Washington, D.C.   F.D.G. WILLIAMS
October 1994

PREFACE

Worthwhile books abound for the American officer interested in learning about his profession. Books on policy-making, strategy, weapons, historic campaigns and battles, biography, and memoirs await the curious soldier, to entertain and enlighten. Some are more useful than others, but a thoughtful reader can derive something of value from most of them. Some were written by participants, some by scholars years after the event. This book is about how someone who was neither a participant nor a scholar wrote books and articles which profoundly influenced the United States Army.

While he never claimed to be a scholar, S.L.A. Marshall would probably argue that he was indeed a participant, for he saw service in both World Wars, Korea, and Vietnam, as well as covering (as a journalist) several other conflicts in which the United States did not engage. Although he was under fire in each, he was not an active combatant in any but the first. Nevertheless, his unique experience is worth studying.

Not a scholar, but a soldier, I became aware of Marshall's writings in my rather random method of studying my profession: browsing through library shelves. When I attended the Armor Officer's Basic Course in 1975, I had never heard of S.L.A. Marshall. But one of my excursions to the library yielded a small book entitled *The Soldier's Load and the Mobility of a Nation*. As a scout platoon leader and again as a company commander, I read General A.S. Collins' *Common Sense Training*, which encouraged soldiers to read for ideas. General Collins specifically mentioned several books and reports, including *The Armed Forces Officer, Men Against Fire,* and *"Notes on Infantry Actions in Korea."* I still did not know Marshall's name, nor did I know that he had written all three of these books. In 1981, back at Fort Knox, I was required to read *Sinai Victory* for a class presentation. Sometime during this year, I became aware that I had been reading Marshall's books for some time without knowing it.

Following the Advanced Course, the Army sent me to graduate school in preparation to teach military history at West Point. At Rice University, my advisor, Dr. Ira Gruber, looked at the list of subjects I was interested in writing my thesis on. The list was headed with "The Influence of S.L.A. Marshall on the United State Army." Because of his recent experience as Morison

Professor at the Command and General Staff College, Dr. Gruber knew that no one had as yet tapped the rather extensive papers of Marshall, housed at the University of Texas at El Paso. Dr. Gruber encouraged me to get permission to work on the subject from Dr. Roger Spiller, who was then planning to write Marshall's biography. Dr. Spiller graciously agreed and got me started.

Before I acknowledge the host of people who helped me, I would like to say two things about what this endeavor has meant to me in the past six years. First, as a soldier, it has caused me to rethink what forces are at work on the battlefield. Although I pray I will not have to put my new thoughts to the test, I hope that, should another conflict come, I will have helped some of those I have touched in my classes and in my writing to survive and win on the battlefield.

Second, I have learned that all men, no matter how famous or well-off, have feet of clay. Marshall, for all his contributions to the Army, was not perfect. As you read this book, remember what the noted British historian John Keegan wrote about Marshall in *The Face of Battle*:

> ... *his ultimate purpose in writing was not merely to describe and analyze—excellent though his description and analysis is—but to persuade the American army that it was fighting its wars the wrong way. It was his conviction that success in battle depended upon structuring the army correctly... he was undoubtedly guilty of over-emphasis and special pleading. His arguments were consonantly effective, so that he has the unusual experience, for a historian, of seeing his message not merely accepted in his lifetime but translated into practice.*

If there be any good to come of this book, I hope that it will cause other soldiers to study their profession, even if they do not agree with everything Marshall had to say.

In the course of this study I have incurred many debts. A legion of professors, soldiers, historians, archivists, and friends provided invaluable insights, time, and other input into this paper. I truly cannot thank them all enough.

I am most obligated to Professor Ira Gruber of Rice University, my advisor and mentor, for his kindness and encouragement without which this project never would have been completed. His guidance throughout was the mainstay of this work. He led me to Dr. Roger Spiller, historian at the U.S.

Army Combat Studies Institute. Dr. Spiller kindly allowed me into his field and directed me to many sources and gave excellent advice.

In the research process, I relied heavily on the outstanding work done at the S.L.A. Marshall Military History Library at the University of Texas, El Paso, by Mr. Thomas Burdett. His patience, knowledge of the material, and ever-helpful attitude made my two trips, many letters, and several phone calls more productive than any researcher could hope. From that came not only valuable documents, but also a list of potential interviewees, the most important of whom was Marshall's widow, Cate. The late Mrs. Marshall gave me several candid interviews and never tried to unduly influence my portrayal of her husband. She led me to still more people to write and interview, including numerous general officers.

I cannot thank all the interviewees by name, but would like to mention Generals A.S. Collins, William J. McCaffrey, E.C. Meyer, H.W.O. Kinnard, William C. Westmoreland, Arthur S. Trudeau, Hamilton H. Howze, Julian Ewell, William R. Desobry, Bruce Palmer, W.E. DePuy, Mark W. Clark, Bruce C. Clarke, James M. Gavin, Aubrey S. Newman, and Richard Cavazos. Others whose interviews provided valuable insights include LTC J.E. Calahan, LTC Robert Fairchild, Robert Leckie, Kenneth Hechler, Dr. Hugh M. Cole, Dr. Forrest Pogue, and Dr. John Westover.

These last three, as Marshall's colleagues and friends, provided frank insights into Marshall's character and abilities that could not be gotten from documents. Further, all through the process, they encouraged and guided me, and spent a great deal of time reviewing the various manuscripts of this paper.

The numerous archivists and historians at the U.S. Army Military History Institute, especially Dr. Richard Sommers, made my short time there most fruitful.

During writing, I had the expert help of my professors, Dr. Gruber, Dr. John F. Guilmartin, and Dr. Frank Haskell. Dr. Guilmartin's observations as a combat veteran and historian, as well as his enthusiastic interest in the subject, made the work come home to me as a professional officer.

After writing, I had the honor of having my paper reviewed by a host of people, including my professors; Mrs. Marshall; Drs. Cole, Pogue, and Westover; Generals Collins and McCaffrey; and historians Commander Thomas B. Buell, Dr. Max Coffman, and Dr. Jesse Stiller.

My heartfelt thanks go to the staff of the TRADOC Command Historian's Office, headed by Dr. H.O. Malone, who heard about my work in a round-about way; Mr. John L. Romjue, whose patient insistence kept me on track in the revision stage; and Dr. Susan Canedy, whose artful diplomacy and expertise as a writer and historian enabled the manuscript to go from an unwieldy mass to a more easily readable form.

Finally I would like to thank my friends at the United States Military Academy for their encouragement, especially LTC Jim Blake and MAJ John F. Shortal. My very special thanks go to John, who, as a professional soldier-historian, and "friend at the front," first told me I had something professional soldiers could benefit from.

Although these and many others made this paper possible, I have no one to blame but myself for any inaccuracies, misinterpretations, or other faults that future research may reveal. There is indeed a great deal more research to be done in this area, especially regarding Marshall's motivations and personal life. Undoubtedly new insights will come to light.

F. D. G. Williams

TABLE OF CONTENTS

Note: Source references are at end of each chapter.

Brigadier General S.L.A. Marshall circa 1960.

INTRODUCTION

S.L.A. Marshall was a soldier, historian, newspaperman, war correspondent, and military critic. His lifetime spanned four of America's wartime periods—World War I, World War II, Korea, Vietnam—and he participated, to some degree, in each one. He wrote extensively, authoring some thirty books, all but four of which dealt with some aspect of the United States Army. He was visible, vociferous, and vexatious. For such a personality it is not surprising to find opinion of him polarized.

At the height of his career in the 1950's, as Major Williams points out in this work, SLAM Marshall could do no wrong. Whispers from the word processors today indicate quite a different tack altogether. And this is not surprising. Any study of Marshall will reveal that for every Marshall admirer there is a detractor—and all are adamant in their opinions. Oddly enough, however, there has been little written about S.L.A. Marshall. Outside of his autobiography, *Bringing Up the Rear*, there is no full-length treatment of his life or his deeds. Fortunately that seems to be changing. At this writing there are several on-going research projects that center on Marshall's life and exploits. Major Williams' work is but the spearhead of what promises to become a very lively debate.

Up until the present time, Sam Marshall's reputation has left him in good stead. He has been considered an eminent military historian, acknowledged by John Keegan, B.H. Liddell Hart, J.F.C. Fuller, Russell Weigley, and Roger Beaumont. Recently, Martin Blumenson, in the June 1989 edition of *Army,* dubbed him one of America's leading experts on military affairs.[1] In July 1989's *Military Review,* General William DePuy lent hearty support to Marshall's findings with similar observations of World War II battlefields.[2]

Marshall wrote prolifically, and his battle narratives—*Pork Chop Hill, Ambush, Bird, Night Drop,* and *Island Victory*—have been widely acclaimed for their realism and veracity. These tributes have been largely the result of the group after-action interview that Marshall developed while covering the

1

assaults with the 27th and 7th Infantry Divisions on the Gilbert and Marshall islands during World War II.

Marshall used this interview technique, assembling a company-minus size group (or smaller) to chronologically trace the military action, to fill in the holes that combat inevitably left. Conducting the interview was, in fact, an act of creating historical records of battle where none existed. These after-action interviews are therefore invaluable in the exploration and subsequent documentation of the events of war. It must be noted that it is not, nor was it ever, touted as *the* sole significant data collection method. Historians in the Historical Branch, created in 1942, practiced this technique in the European and Pacific Theaters of Operations. In conjunction with other, more traditional documentation, the group interview became one of the methodologies that comprised the research for the multi-volumned *The US Army In World War II* series. The acceptance of the group interview technique resulted in Marshall's employment by the U.S. government during the Korean and Vietnam wars, as well as by the Israelis following the 1956 Arab-Israeli war, to teach the procedure to Army historians.

The after-action group interview technique, and the conclusions Marshall drew from this research methodology, are now coming under harsh fire as researchers begin their probe of the past. Of chief concern is Marshall's bold 25 percent firing ratio that was publicized in *Men Against Fire* in 1947. Very simply, Marshall wrote that during World War II, only one out of every four infantry riflemen fired their weapons. Curiously, little ado over this assertion was made in the 1950s. Comments from the field indicated that this percentage accurately reflected most soldiers' memories of their battlefield experience.

Today, however, some authors are questioning this figure. Among them are Dr. Roger Spiller, Professor of Combined Arms Warfare at Fort Leavenworth, Kansas; and Mr. Harold P. Leinbaugh, World War II veteran and author of *The Men of Company K*. Spiller, in a winter 1988 *RUSI* article, takes exception to the 25 percent firing ratio because of the data and methodology on which it was based.[3] Notably, Spiller asserts, there wasn't any. He can find no statistical data whatsoever to confirm Marshall's 25 percent firing ratio. Checking Marshall's available field notebooks and other written documentation, Spiller concluded that the 25 percent figure was fabricated. He deplores Marshall's lack of scholarship, noting that his conclusions were based on personal knowledge and observations drawn from his own military experience that was, according to Spiller, dubious at best and dependent upon those who participated in the group interviews.

Harold Leinbaugh is more forceful in his criticism of Marshall. As "one who was there," Leinbaugh admittedly feels personally insulted by the 25 percent firing ratio, believing it to be an unfair condemnation of U.S. infantry riflemen in World War II. [4] He echoes Spiller's reservations concerning the apparent lack of historical evidence and goes further to assert that in many instances in Marshall's autobiography Marshall has not told the truth. This accusation is in direct reference to Marshall's accounts of his First World War wartime experience and his military record. Leinbaugh asserts that Marshall did not participate in the Meuse-Argonne, St. Mihiel, or Soissons campaigns as his autobiography notes. According to Leinbaugh, Marshall was a sergeant in the 315th Engineers who spent his tour digging roads and building delousing stations.

Much of the debate concerning Marshall could be laid to rest quite easily with solid research, or even a careful reading of *Men Against Fire*, were it not for the fact that Marshall was not all he said he was. Some of Marshall's claims to fame stretch the truth, or worse. For instance, Marshall claims to have won a battlefield commission during WWI. In reality, he was commissioned a lieutenant several months after the armistice. Along the same line, he maintains, and his military record reflects, that he completed two years of college at the Texas School of Mines (now the University of Texas at El Paso). The University's records indicate he completed only one semester. These sorts of discrepancies are the basis for Leinbaugh's charges of fraud.

Most people who knew or worked with Marshall admit that he was not a stranger to oversimplification, exaggeration, or manipulation. Marshall's critics, at least, believe that one marked as America's foremost military historian should not be discovered to have lied about his military record, for to do so, and then pretentiously point out problems in the force, is the ultimate fraud.That, however, is not the focal point of this work. Sam Marshall under the historical microscope does not look like the Sam Marshall portrayed in his autobiography. That should surprise no one. Does that mean that his observations of World War II—as written in *Men Against Fire* and *The Soldier's Load*, his two most noted works, should be automatically discounted?

Do the discrepancies noted by his critics impact upon Marshall's postulations and observations as put forward in *Men Against Fire* and *The Soldier's Load*? The fact is, they did not. Impact from these two works, regardless of the author and his nature or motivations, is still felt today. Major Williams maintains that S.L.A. Marshall was one of the U.S. Army's movers and shakers. He was a catalyst for change when change was badly needed. And the fact of the matter is, change was implemented. Marshall did indeed make a mark. His observations, proposed changes, and actions taken as a result make up the heart of this work. As such, it reflects more than just the experiences of one man. It is a chronicle of positive movement by our fighting force—an intensely interesting story for those whose interests lie with our warfighting capability and how we achieve and maintain it.

Susan Canedy

1. Martin Blumenson, "Did 'Slam' Guess at Fire Ratios? Probably: A Legend Remembered," *Army* (June 1989): p. 16.

2. William E. DePuy, "Insights," *Military Review* (July 1989): p. 96-98.

3. Roger J. Spiller, "S.L.A. Marshall and the Ratio of Fire," *RUSI Journal* (Winter 1988): p. 63-71.

4. Philip Gold, "Flak for a Man and His Claim That Few Soldiers Open Fire," *Insight* (March 27, 1989): 18-19; Fredric Smoler, " The Secret of the Soldiers Who Didn't Shoot," *American Heritage* 40/2 (March 1989): p. 40-45.

CHAPTER ONE

JOURNALISTIC BEGINNINGS

*G*ood God, you must be dumber than I thought. Your initials spell *SLAM, and you don't realize that's money in the bank? It's perfect for a sports editor. It's perfect for anything. Nobody can forget that name.*

Tad Dorgan

When America entered World War II in 1941, a forty-one year old newspaperman with no formal education beyond high school but with a remarkable talent for telling good stories volunteered for active duty. As a civilian whose active military experience was limited to going off to war as a teenager, he had little to offer beyond his energy and his writing skills. Yet within two years, he had begun to influence the way the United States Army approached military history. Before the end of the decade, he had contributed to and advanced the studies of military leadership, tactics, and psychology. How could a single civilian cause such a stir? Was it skill? Luck? Genius? It was all of these and more.

Who was this man and what was his background? He was Samuel Lyman Atwood Marshall, the son of a brickmaker, brought up in El Paso, Texas. In a sketch of Marshall's career, certain elements of his personality stand out. Marshall was flamboyant, ambitious, gregarious, arrogant, and seemingly indomitable. He was what some people would call a "character." Upon meeting him, one was either charmed by his wit or repulsed by his occasional social abrasiveness. This contrast served to gain him many allies, as well as many enemies, in his crusade to reform the Army.

Marshall's hallmark was his keenness for detail and his eye for the dramatic. He was adept at telling a story full of color and excitement, a story which often focused on the activities of common people accomplishing uncommon things. Such stories found their way into volumes of articles and books which caught the interest of many and served as Marshall's vehicle for presenting his ideas and insights. The color and simplicity of his writing style assured him a strong following. Without this dramatic and yet simple style, he could not have contributed as much as he did to military affairs.

Another aspect of his personality which made his later success possible was his boldness. Repeatedly Marshall faced situations which demanded a decision, the results of which would have important repercussions. Very often he could have made the safe choice—the one which would not have required him to place his life or reputation on the line. His habitual response, however, was to dare to risk—to march forward where others might have hesitated. Life to him was a gamble. Without taking risks nothing could be gained. Often, because he refused to stand back and let events take their own course, he had a significant impact on subsequent developments. For instance, his efforts at keeping the historical officers on duty in Europe in the face of rapid demobilization after World War II was a result of just this kind of activity. Without the presence and continued activities of his group, the excellent *The United States Army in World War II* historical series would never have achieved the distinction it did.

Marshall's effectiveness was also due to his innate gregariousness. Drawn to Marshall for whatever reason, a variety of people sought his friendship and camaraderie. Marshall used these contacts in his many endeavors. They gave him not only the moral support necessary to sustain him, but also information which was difficult to obtain, introductions which led to more friendships, and resources which made it possible to gather more information. Largely because of his vast network of friends and acquaintances in many professions and on many levels, Marshall could make the most of rapidly unfolding events—he could almost make his own luck.

Marshall's personality was dominated by a strong will—a trait which proved to be a double-edged sword. On the one hand, his ambition drove him ever to strive in the face of opposition. While he was writing about the courage of the common soldier, the public preferred the wonders of technology. While the government sank vast sums into atomic weapons, Marshall preached that weapons were only as good as the men behind them. On the other hand, while his ambition drove him forward, his ego held him back. It was an obstacle to his success because people often reacted negatively to his rough, boisterous, and sometimes rude ways. Some were put off by his pontifications and arrogant predictions. Had he been a mild-mannered commentator, he would never have had such problems—nor would he have had such influence.

A final element in Marshall's character involved his prolific output. At the peak of his career, he was writing a syndicated newspaper column, articles for military journals, and historical narratives of recent battles. He spoke to the public on the radio and to the Army in lecture halls. He appeared before congressional committees and Kiwanis clubs. And before every audience he preached the same gospel: this is a great nation and we are a great people, but certain aspects of our military have to change and we must change them now. A man with less energy and weaker powers of concentration could not have kept up such a pace or reached as many people.

How did Marshall develop as he did? What events in his early life affected or presaged what he was to become? Forrest Pogue, eminent military historian and biographer of another famous Marshall, provided a fitting warning for anyone trying to draw too certain a conclusion from a man's childhood:

> *What sort of boy was he? What promise did he show? These are questions no biographer can answer with any assurance. The records are always scant and the temptation to find the lineaments of greatness already prefigured in the child. For Marshall, the records—that is, contemporary testimony—are almost wholly missing. Almost all that can be reported of the boy is what the man at the age of seventy-six recalled and chose to reveal. This then is a chapter of memories.*[1]

The same can be said of this chapter, based as it is on S.L.A. Marshall's memoirs *Bringing Up the Rear*, edited by his widow and published after his death.

Sam Marshall grew up in the wild and woolly town of El Paso. It is difficult now for us to imagine what early twentieth-century life in this small border town was like for a young boy. Though Texas had enjoyed statehood for over sixty years, trouble with Mexico continued. Civil war and revolution spilled over into the border towns in the form of raids by such men as the notorious Pancho Villa. Because Villa spent a great deal of time in Ciudad Juarez, across the Rio Grande from El Paso, it was inevitable that a curious young Sam Marshall would occasionally venture into Mexico to taste the adventure and excitement of a lawless town. It would not be far off the mark to consider El Paso still a "wild west" town, with all the images of gunfighters, saloons, and loose women which the term brings to mind. It was in such surroundings that Sam grew up.

It was here, as a boy of fifteen, that Sam Marshall was first introduced to the United States Army. Eating daily at a mess hall at nearby Camp Cotton, he came to know the soldiers of the first American unit to suffer casualties in World War I. Of his associations with these regulars, Marshall would later write:

> *My main contacts were with the enlisted men... I enjoyed the association with those old pros all the way. They did not talk down to me or seek to embarrass me, and I enjoyed their friendly conversation over the following months. While associating with them did not really draw me to the military, it had the residual benefit that at age fifteen I lost all fear of being in the infantry. Whereas nearly every youth regards the army with a little awe and trembling, though he is loathe to admit it, the men of F Company helped make my putting on a soldier suit a quite natural thing.*[2]

At a very impressionable age, Marshall formed a view of life in the Army from the soldier's perspective—a view he would later draw on and add to.

Besides his early connection with the Army, life in El Paso had other influences on the growing boy. Something about the town encouraged the teenagers to ignore schoolwork and concentrate on having fun. Enamoured of girls and games, young Sam decided that he would forego homework and place his academic career in the hands of his memory by paying close attention in class. He attributes his later abilities of concentration and memorization to this decision.[3] While he was honing these skills, he twice failed high school history. But one thing his teacher said stayed with him throughout his life: "Forget about the dates and personages. The object of studying history is that we may learn from its processes. Either we do, or we repeat our mistakes."[4] He remembered this years later in the Pacific when he insisted that the Army could learn from what he was finding out as an historian.

Yet another result of his living in that rough and tumble world was the development of a certain quality which is sometimes called, in another place and time, being "street-wise." He learned in El Paso that a quick wit, a strong will, a bit of bluff and bluster, and a lot of daring made the difference between success and failure. To survive in such an atmosphere, much less thrive in it, he developed a sixth sense for dealing with others, knowing when to apply tact and when to apply pressure.[5]

El Paso had the stuff of which legends were made: action, violence, colorful characters, and a long history. In the days before radio and television, telling stories and listening to them took up much of the free time of children. Sam must have had ample opportunity as a lad to hear master storytellers spin a web of suspense and adventure. As he got older and began to make his living as a journalist, words became his stock in trade, and he may very well have drawn upon his early experiences to judge what did and what did not work in capturing the attention of an audience.[6]

When the United States entered World War I, Sam was still in high school. In November 1917, he enlisted and soon found himself undergoing a routine quite different from the easy-going, rambling life of a student in a one-horse town. He hated the regimentation inherent in the military, especially the spit and polish. His self-discipline and strength enabled him to handle with ease the adjustment to the physical and mental demands of the service, but he never developed a high regard for parades, inspection, or, most of all, getting up early:

> *When I joined the Army in 1917, I found that everything in the military to my delighted amazement was strangely easy for me, with one exception—reveille. That song of Berlin's, "Oh, How I Hate to Get Up in the Morning," had been written just for me.*

So I started looking about for ways to beat reveille and discovered that by putting in for school duty, I could avoid all formations. Hence I applied, and because practically no one else was playing eager beaver, I got it. I went to grenade school, demolitions school, bayonet school, topographical school and infantry specialist school. By the end of seven months I was the best qualified NCO in the Regiment. My superiors thought this was proof of great diligence on my part. Not so, I was simply looking for a chance to get more sleep, though I kept that secret to myself.[7]

All of this training was put to the test on the battlefields of Europe. For over four months, Marshall saw action with the AEF in the Soissons, St. Mihiel, and Meuse-Argonne campaigns and toward the end of the war attended an officer candidate school. He received his commission to second lieutenant and stayed on in Europe. His first assignment was as an instructor at the Infantry Candidates' School at La Valbonne, then as a company commander of "casuals" (men being returned to the U.S. from hospitals), later as the commander of Depot Service Company No. 64 near Le Mans, and finally as commander of a stevedore company in Brest. His participation as a front line soldier and as a junior officer in the post-armistice Army afforded him many opportunities to observe the behavior, policies, and procedures of a military force. He noted inefficiencies in supply, absurdities of regulation, and oddities in performance. An astute observer of human nature even at eighteen, Marshall wondered why men marching eleven miles to the front reached their trenches dead tired, and why six weeks later those same men marching away from the front would march three times as far and arrive as if it had been "a breeze."[8] These "problems" he would store, unbeknownst even to himself, for future consideration.

When he left active duty in September 1919, Marshall had a hard time settling back down. His horizons, like those of countless others who had gone off to war, had been broadened beyond the life awaiting him. He tried going to college, for though he had not graduated from high school, the Texas School of Mines (later the University of Texas at El Paso) allowed returning officers to enter without a high school diploma. But Marshall did not finish and wandered from job to job for the next three years.

While watching an Armistice Day parade in 1922, Marshall felt deeply depressed. Untrained and unprepared for life outside the military, he did not seem to be making much of himself. He owed three thousand dollars, had no job, and worse yet, had no prospects of any. Realizing that he was standing before the offices of the *El Paso Herald*, Marshall decided he had nothing to lose and went in to apply for a job. With a display of what would later become typical Marshall bravado, he managed to impress the editor:

> *The pay range was from twenty to forty-five dollars a week, depending on experience.*
>
> *"Mr. Martin," I said, "I'd like to start at forty-five."*
>
> *That brought him from his chair.*
>
> *He waggled his finger at me and shouted, "Are you crazy? You have just talked yourself out of any chance to start."*
>
> *"No," I answered him, "I'm remarkably sane at this moment. I happen to be three thousand dollars in debt and have a family to support. If I start at twenty-five or so, my creditors will be on my neck and I will be pestering you. That will finish me. But at forty-five, I can begin paying off, and they'll see the wisdom of easing off. If I haven't made good in thirty days, I'd expect to be fired. So the most you can lose is two hundred."*
>
> *He pondered for all of two minutes. "It sounds like a sporting proposition. You're on. Just don't tell anyone how much money you're making."*
>
> *"When do I start?"*
>
> *"Right now."*
>
> *Hallelujah! I had become a reporter.*[9]

The next day he was off to a promising start with a story on the front page, thanks to another typical Marshall talent: being lucky enough to be in the right place at the right time.

Within a month, still on the payroll, Marshall decided that being a good reporter meant that he must be able to write not only about local events but also about politics, sports, the economy, and humor. But realizing also that a successful reporter must have a special talent, he made a crucial career decision:

> *Within the next hour on that same day I had my formula, my plan for my professional life. In foreign affairs, instead of following the crowd and educating myself on Europe or the Pacific, I would specialize in Mexico and the Central American states. That way, I would get a crack at a revolution more or less regularly. Finally, I would train myself to be a military critic. The goal would necessitate much home study and the building of a special library, but once I made it, I would have practically no competition in this country.*[10]

Whether or not his decision reflected quite as much forethought and wisdom as these words from his memoirs imply, he did indeed embark upon at least the beginnings of his life's path. Because of this decision, he was to have two parallel, often simultaneous careers: one as a journalist, and another as a soldier.

Within a few months, he was writing a regular sports column for the paper and in his own time pursuing the study of war. During his time as a sports writer, he reached a daily output of four thousand words, a pace which he continued throughout his life. Believing that "writing is not a gift or an art but a willingness to accept the required self-discipline," Marshall seldom let a day go by in his adult life that he did not sit down to write even if he felt "the well was dry."[11] This talent to produce became Marshall's claim to fame. His fast-paced and humorous prose earned him a living as a journalist and would serve him well as military historian and analyst.

One newspaperman who knew Marshall later in life provided great insights into Marshall's character and his qualifications for what he came to do. Mr. Dale Walker, a reporter for many years, met Marshall when the latter returned to El Paso to retire. Walker, now with the *Texas Western Press* in El Paso, suggested that Marshall's training as a reporter in a rough and tumble town like El Paso shaped his approach to his later job as combat historian—and indeed to his subsequent roles as military analyst and spokesman for the military.

First, perhaps, came his focus on people. Newspapers are written for people to witness the struggle of man against the forces assailing him.

A winning story is one which tells dramatically of the little man triumphing over odds. "With Sam's background and ability as a newspaperman, he had it as part of his writing philosophy that you can't go far wrong in a book or essay if you center it about the human condition... His books are no more than extended superb reportage."[12]

Second, two personality traits enabled Marshall throughout his life to excel as a reporter: persistence and gumption. Again and again in his career, he refused to be cowed by obstacles or risks or lack of precedent. He often stood virtually alone on matters large and small. His famous book, *Men Against Fire,* was practically a one-man-stand against the widespread post-World War II tendency to believe in the supremacy of technology in modern war. While it delved into the psychological factors involved in combat, this misunderstood book represented Marshall's firm conviction that the emphasis on nuclear weapons and other tools of destruction was in danger of undermining the crucial human element in warfare.

To such persistence, Marshall added gumption—that quality which allows a reporter to insinuate himself into certain affairs (and into the lives of certain people) despite the potential for rebuff or failure. Marshall's life, from his first day as a newspaper reporter to his days as an observer in Vietnam, in volved getting to know influential people, offering his advice (solicited or not), and acting quickly to seize whatever opportunities fate presented him. Above all, he displayed initiative and self-reliance in all that he did.

Besides personal qualities, Marshall developed certain skills as a reporter which would serve him well in his military career. Every good newspaperman cultivates sources. That is, even when a particular story is written, he will maintain contact with those who may provide insight, or even better an "in", to a later event. Indeed the officers Marshall interviewed about the Battle of the Bulge in 1945 were the very men who hosted him in Vietnam in the 1960s.

As a sports writer in El Paso, Marshall developed a keen interviewing technique. An effective interview involves considerably more than just asking questions from a prepared list, more than knowing the subject matter well. Perhaps the first requisite of a good interview is to put the subject at ease, to make him comfortable, to cause him to speak freely. But once the interviewee has opened up, there is still more for the reporter to do. First rate interviewers have a sixth sense for the subtleties and nuances of the interviewee's responses. He must listen for not only what is said, but also for what is not said. For instance, he must detect changes in the degree of self-assurance, as exhibited in the tone of voice, in the length of pauses, in the fidgiting of hands. He must know when to press an issue and when to back off. All these things and more a good interviewer must master. Part of it comes with experience. Part does not.

Related to his ability to sense the interviewee's non-verbal messages, a good reporter must trust his intuition. He must act when there are only hints of a story. Like a detective, he must put clues together and try to see through the fog of extraneous data, through the mist of half-truths, and through the darkness of incomplete information. Like an historian, he must try to recreate a story even when the causal relationships are only dimly seen. In short, he must rely on more than hard facts. He must dare to speak what he believes to be the truth, even when others may dispute his interpretation of the available information.

Another of Marshall's important skills was the ability to write rapidly under any condition. Part of a newsman's daily fare is meeting deadlines. A newspaperman learns to operate in any condition and to produce copy regardless of the commotion going on about him. Just as a postman gets the job done through rain, hail, sleet, and gloom of night, so also does a newspaperman write amid the noise, clamor, and excitement of the newsroom. He has to. The deadline reigns supreme.

Not everyone can concentrate in such a chaotic environment. Marshall's powers of concentration would be tested from the Pacific Isles to the forests of Europe. Unlike some writers, he did not have to be closeted in the quiet of a room or office. He could write on an improvised desk in the open field. And he could write fast. A close companion of his during World War II wrote in his diary about Marshall's habits of writing: "I worked late again because my progress has been slow. Colonel Marshall expects me to keep up with him. I can't, but I try to come in at least a poor second. How that guy does work!"[13] He would frequently work late into the night to get a report in on time the next morning.

Yet one should not believe that he had always wanted to write. He considered it a fortuitous accident that he took up journalism. He was a maverick in the business, for he sought action.

> *The journalism game was still exciting but never soul-satisfying. It left an empty feeling, being a mirror of life and not the living of it. Above all, from first to last, I objected to most of the members of my craft because they were sideliners rather than activists.*[14]

So Marshall found himself in love with his work, while thinking that most other writers were less than productive members of society. He worked himself hard and expected those that worked for him to work hard, too. His personal traits and his skills admirably suited him for his tasks as reporter and later, as combat historian. While he would not venture the opinion that he was born to the trade, he did stay with it, and his first years on the *El Paso Herald* laid the groundwork for his later endeavors. In *Parameters*, the journal of the Army War College, a close friend and associate wrote:

> *The years with the El Paso Herald were crucial to Marshall's career. Fort Bliss was a way-station for a host of Army officers who would rise to high rank. Here Marshall made Army friendships that lasted for life. In these years, too, he commenced to read military history as a conscious process of self-education in the military art. But most important, in these years, were the rough-and-tumble associations formed by a tough editor in the frontier environment of West Texas. Marshall became involved with the "outlaw" baseball teams formed in defiance of Judge Kenesaw Landis... helped manage the football teams sponsored by the mining companies, and he wrote the wire stories on once-great pugilists making their last fights in the Juarez Bull Ring. It would be said of Marshall in later years that he had mastered the art of communicating with the common soldier, of whatever race or social status, on a footing of mutual respect, and with compassion and understanding. No Army career course in the psychology of leadership could have given Marshall the finely-honed ability to perceive the varieties of human response to life and death, challenge and despair, danger and fatigue, which he developed in the West Texas years.*[15]

Marshall's love for a good story with a human interest angle began in this period. He would later concentrate on the underdog, the soldier with a speech impediment or some other abnormality. One of the repeated themes in Marshall's subsequent writings about war was that the common man, no matter what others thought of him, had a certain dignity and courage which often came out only in the trying circumstances of battle.

Having become the city editor by the time the *El Paso Herald* folded in 1927, Marshall got a job on the *Detroit News*. A large newspaper in a large city, the *News* became Marshall's home until 1961. The editors of the *News* were instrumental in his development. Allowing him to write on any subject he cared to, they helped him build that all around talent he had identified earlier as requisite for a successful columnist. They also allowed him to travel south of the border to cover the occasional small revolution, and, in 1936, to Spain for the Spanish Civil War, which he covered from the Loyalist side. Over the years, his editors gave him leave to serve with the military, realizing that a good story or two was certain to come of every such endeavor.

In the 1930s, Marshall began writing seriously on military matters. He had been reading works by such eminent military thinkers as J.F.C. Fuller and Basil Henry Liddell Hart and was greatly impressed by their theories. J.F.C. Fuller learned of Marshall's interest just before the war and began a correspondence which lasted for more than thirty years. It was through an article on the future of mechanized forces which Marshall wrote for the *Infantry Journal* in the late thirties that brought him to Fuller's attention. Fuller wondered where Marshall had gotten the ideas for his article. Marshall replied that Fuller's *Lectures on Field Service Regulations III: Operations Between Mechanized Forces (FSR III)* was his primary source. Fuller wrote back, "My Dear Boy, so far as I know you are the only person in the United States or Britain who is taking me seriously."[16] Fuller was so pleased that he made Marshall his literary agent in the United States.[17] Evidence of their growing friendship appeared immediately. When Marshall's second book, *Armies on Wheels*, came out in 1941, General Fuller wrote the foreword; and Fuller not only asked Marshall to write the foreword for the American edition of *BFSR III,* which appeared in 1943, but also dedicated his *Machine Warfare*, published in that same year, to Marshall. In honor of his two British mentors, Fuller and Liddell Hart, Marshall dedicated his 1963 work, *Battle at Best,* "To my great and good friends, two wise men in the art of warfare, J.F.C. Fuller and B.H. Liddell Hart, who have helped me immeasurably though the years." He also had Fuller write the foreword for that book.

As for Liddell Hart, Marshall wrote him in 1942, requesting a copy of his *The British Way in Warfare,* which was difficult to get in the United States. Liddell Hart replied, but that was their last correspondence until after the war.[18] Visiting Liddell Hart after the war, Marshall told "the Captain" how much his writings had meant to him as a young journalist in the twenties, trying to develop knowledge of the military art. Liddell Hart's reaction caught Marshall off guard:

> *He looked at me from his great height and said almost mournfully, "Slam, why in heaven's name didn't you ever tell me? I had no idea you drew anything from my work. I thought it was all Fuller." I felt sudden shame. He was right. I had never said one word in praise.*[19]

Through his correspondence with these two innovative thinkers, Marshall developed an abiding understanding of military affairs. Although much of his early writing on warfare was derivative, not original, Marshall paved the way for Fuller and Liddell Hart in America. Like them, Marshall wrote prolifically about the military, challenging it to improve its effectiveness, while supporting it against its detractors in the legislative and public arenas. Such friendships as theirs provided a degree of reinforcement necessary to bear the wounds and cries of outraged officials and citizens.

Another friendship which would reap great dividends blossomed about this time as well. Marshall's writings for the *Infantry Journal* brought him to that publication's editor, Colonel Joseph I. Greene. Greene backed Marshall for years and helped him get his start in the publishing world. Several of Marshall's early books were published under the auspices of the Infantry Journal Press and its successor, the Combat Forces Press.

By the time the United States entered World War II, Sam Marshall had some forty years of rich experiences. El Paso, Detroit, and Europe at war had molded a man and cultivated within him a dual passion. Sam Marshall's life would be spent crusading for that institution which he had come to love, the U.S. Army, by means of his chosen avocation of newspaperman. The two roles—soldier and reporter—would juxtapose so completely that each identity would become lost in the other. It was no surprise, therefore, to find that when Japan attacked Pearl Harbor, Sam Marshall wanted to put on an olive drab uniform and set off with the troops.

1. Forrest C. Pogue, *George C. Marshall: Education of a General* (New York: The Viking Press, 1963), p. 17. Dr. Pogue's comments apply as well for S.L.A. Marshall as for George C. Marshall, even to the age of memory, for the younger Marshall died in his seventy-sixth year while working on his autobiography, *Bringing Up the Rear.*

2. S.L.A. Marshall, *Bringing Up the Rear* (San Raphael, California: Presidio Press, 1979), p. 6.

3. Ibid., p. 8.

4. Ibid., p. 9

5. Hugh M. Cole, untitled manuscript, 13 January 1978. Supplied to the author by Dr. John Westover.

6. Marshall would look back on these times with a great deal of pleasure, so much so that he retired in El Paso.

7. S.L.A. Marshall, "On Being Commissioned: The Commissioning Day Address at University of Virginia, Charlottesville," June 7, 1969, p. 12, published in booklet form with two other speeches under the title *The Last Refuge.*

8. S.L.A. Marshall, "The Human Equation in Combat," *S.L.A. Marshall at Leavenworth,* Roger J. Spiller, ed. (Fort Leavenworth, Kansas: U.S. Army Command and General Staff College, 1980), Lecture III, p. 10. Hereafter referred to as Spiller Lectures.

9. Marshall, *Bringing Up the Rear,* p. 18.

10. Ibid., p. 20.

11. Ibid., p. 23.

12. Interview with Dave Walker, 22 July 1986.

13. John G. Westover, "Describing the Colonel," *Newsletter of the S.L.A. Marshall Military History Collection,* Number 11, Summer 1985, p. 1.

14. Marshall, *Bringing Up the Rear,* p. 24.

15. Hugh M. Cole, "S.L.A. Marshall (1900-1977): In Memoriam," *Parameters,* Vol. VIII, No. 1 (March 1978): 2-3.

16. Marshall, *Bringing Up the Rear,* p. 30.

17. Letter from Dr. Forrest C. Pogue to the author, 9 August 1983.

18. Eventually 141 letters passed between the two before Liddell Hart died in 1970. Roger J. Spiller, "The Marshall—Liddell Hart Correspondence," *Newsletter of the S.L.A. Marshall Military History Collection,* January 1984, p. 1.

19. Marshall, *Bringing Up the Rear,* p. 31.

CHAPTER TWO

FROM JOURNALIST TO COMBAT HISTORIAN

T *he dust churned up by Patton's tanks does less to distort perspective*
than the dust raised by the archivist as he thumbs through records
half a century old.

Dr. Hugh M. Cole

In June 1942, Sam Marshall was called to Washington as a civilian con-sultant to Secretary of War Henry Stimson. In September he was commis-sioned a major and assigned to the Orientation Section of the Information Branch of the General Staff.[1] In this position he helped write the *Small Guides to Foreign Countries* series, which was designed to aid American troops stationed abroad, and helped establish the Army News Service. He was also instrumental in the development of the policy for the relocation of the Japanese Americans on the West Coast. This included the recruiting of the 442nd Nisei Combat Team. With a great deal of assistance from several others, Marshall not only wrote this unprecedented policy but also par-ticipated in its implementation.[2]

Shortly after finishing this task, Marshall was directed to begin writing a series of pamphlets describing the battles in which American forces were par-ticipating. The direction came from General George C. Marshall, Chief of

Staff of the Army, who had decided to distribute the pamphlets to the American wounded. When Sam Marshall told his boss that no one in the War Department could provide the kind of information required to make the pamphlets readable, his director balked, saying that he could not go to the Chief of Staff with that news. Marshall said he would go, and with a boldness that had become second nature, he did.

General Marshall reacted to this information with aplomb, merely asking Major Marshall what the Historical Section of the General Staff was doing. The major replied, "Sir, it is still bogged down researching World War I."[3] General Marshall made a few notes and dismissed the writer by telling him he could forget about the pamphlets.

In his memoirs, Sam Marshall suggests that because of this brief interview, General Marshall created a new historical section. It is more likely that the journalist in uniform had confirmed what the general already knew. The coverage of the war was behind schedule, and the Army needed a crew of dedicated scholars and writers to keep up with events.

As early as March 1942 the creation of a new historical branch had been proposed to centralize historical activities and begin the preparatory work of a large-scale operational history to be written at the end of the war.[4] Designated the Historical Branch and operating within the G-2 of the General Staff, this new agency was formally established on 20 July 1943 under the direction of Lieutenant Colonel John Mason Kemper.[5] In September, Kemper was joined by Sam Marshall and five others. Their first specific tasking was to prepare brief studies of military operations according to the Chief of Staff's earlier request.[6]

The Historical Branch was responsible for establishing and maintaining historical organizations in each theater of operations, providing historical officers to supervise the accumulation of documents, and researching and writing the operational histories of the ongoing war.[7] Given no further guidance and permitted considerable autonomy, Kemper proposed sending nine three-man teams overseas to supervise the maintenance and collection of unit records and to interview participants of specific combat engagements.

In October 1943, Marshall set off for the Pacific to participate, as historian, in the up-coming invasion of the Gilbert Islands.[8] Stopping first in Oahu where the 27th Division was stationed, he presented himself to the commander and managed to secure a free pass forward. He was briefed on the operation and embarked with the Division on the transport. During this time, to satisfy his reporter's curiosity, he and the Division G-4 had the expedition weighed—not only the equipment carried by the individual soldier, but the entire cargo, including the thirty day fuel supply.[9]

When the troops stormed the beaches of Makin Island in November 1943, Marshall followed several waves ashore. Accompanying men into combat and observing them under fire provided him with information on the behavior of a fighting force. His experiences in the field, which would later bring him to a position of reknown, occasionally taught him basic lessons of the human condition. For example, trailing a battalion onto the island of Makin:

> *I followed along for about a hundred yards into the bush. There, after just a few stumbling steps, I fell apart. My senses reeled. I was hit by such weakness that I dropped my carbine and could not unbuckle my belt, but that was not the worst of it. Within seconds my nerve had gone completely and I shook all over from fear.*
>
> *I lay flat under a pandanus tree, telling myself: "It's combat fatigue. You've been kidding yourself. You are too old for the wars." Being unable to walk, and scarcely able to think, I decided to stay where I was, wait for a stretcher-bearer to come along and get me back to the Calvert where I would stay...*
>
> *Before any aid man came my way, a rifleman stopped and stared at me. Then he took a bottle of pills from his jacket and downed a couple of them.*
>
> *I asked weakly, "What you got?"*
>
> *"Salt."*
>
> *"Gimme some. Nothing can make me feel worse than I do."*
>
> *He gave me the bottle ... I washed down eleven salt tablets with the lukewarm water from my canteen. ...Within the next ten minutes my nerve and strength were fully restored, and I was never again troubled; yet that lesson had to be learned the hard way. No one had ever told me that one consequence of dehydration is cowardice in its most abject form.[10]*

Once recovered, Marshall got down to the business at hand, that of writing an accurate history of the assault on Makin. His efforts seemed doomed. Neither observing events for himself, nor talking to troops after the action, nor watching the marks on the situation map at headquarters later gave him satisfaction. His own observations and those of others engaged in the actions were distorted. Marks on a map deceived even the most seasoned officer.

The solution fell into his lap quite accidently while he accompanied still another battalion in its sweep to the far tip of the island. Covering only three miles in the torturous tropical heat during their afternoon advance, the soldiers were too tired to dig in for the night. Without realizing it, they had come to rest only a few hundred yards from the camp of the last large group of Japanese soldiers remaining on Makin. During the night, the enemy charged the perimeter eleven times. Each time they were thrown back. By morning, it was evident that the single most crucial part in the drama was played by a young machinegunner who could only be extracted by the combined efforts of two tanks and a rifle platoon.[11] That the fate of the unit rested on the efforts of a very few stalwart souls could not be denied. Marshall saw in this incident an opportunity to search for the truth in a contained action whose players were few and whose duration was definite.

That morning, as the sweep continued to the tip of the island, the battalion commander confided to Marshall that he did not have a clear picture of the evening's action. Consequently, at noon, when they reached the end of the island and the fighting was done, Marshall sent for the machinegunner and his platoon leader. It was time to recount the events of the battle and hopefully record some accurate history.

As the session got underway, the lieutenant said that he had ordered Schwartz, the machinegunner,

> ... *to take over the gun; (but) Schwartz insisted that the lieutenant was nowhere around and that he had done it on his own. Finally, to get at the truth, Marshall lined up the entire battalion and asked each man to report everything he had seen and done during the night. Not only was Schwartz's story upheld, but Marshall almost immediately realized he had stumbled onto the secret of*

accurate combat reporting. Every man remembered something—a piece to be fitted into the jigsaw puzzle.[12]

Thus was born the after-action combat interview technique.

Aboard ship and later in Hawaii, Marshall conducted more mass interviews until he put together the picture of the island fight. He also wrote the first plan for conducting group interviews. This was included in a report to Kemper begun on 7 December and finished a month later. This document illustrated the practical role of the historical officer in gathering intelligence about the enemy. It also demonstrated the value of learning about one's own units. Knowledge of one's own strengths and weaknesses could be had, thereby accomplishing one of the most famous yet most misunderstood dicta of Sun Tzu: know thyself.

Marshall's format did not make its way to Kemper in Washington soon enough to become the basis for the training of the newly-arrived members of the field historical teams. The first batch had to make do with an extremely off-the-cuff reading program designed by the only one of them that had any claim to being an experienced military historian, Hugh Cole. However, the first group that Kemper sent out had heard a great deal about Marshall, for Forrest Pogue remembered:

*I remember reading articles by Sam Marshall before I got in the Army in April 1942... When I joined the Historical Section of the War Department in March 1944, ... we heard a lot about Sam since some eight or ten of us had been brought in as the first combat historians to be sent overseas... We took a three week course on combat interviewing with Cole as instructor. We heard a lot about Sam's work in interrogation in the Pacific. His book, **Island Victory**, based on his interviews at Kwajalein, was on the way to be printed. We heard a lot about the fact that he was in on some of the island battles and afterward when men in the units had little to do [aboard ship], he interviewed large numbers of them at a time.*[13]

Marshall's new method impressed not only the Historical Branch, but also the leaders of the units that he had interviewed. The commander of the 27th Division, Major General Ralph C. Smith, wrote to the Assistant Chief of

Staff, G-2, under whose purview the Historical Branch fell:

[Colonel Marshall] gathered what appears to me to be highly important data. His tact and keenness as an observer made him a most valuable member of the expedition.

It seems to me that the pattern he has set for collecting historical data on the spot should be of the greatest value, both to the Army in its present training problems and to the future for basic historical data.

If the Historical Division can send officers on such missions who are the equivalent of Colonel Marshall in judgment and tact, I think they will always be welcomed by commanders.[14]

Smith realized that the data which Marshall had collected could be put to immediate use in fighting the Japanese. For example, Marshall had noticed that when a tank platoon was not subordinated to the infantry unit it was attached to, it would often leave an engagement before the enemy was defeated, thereby depriving its infantry contingent of heavy weapons. Investigating one such action, Marshall determined that the tank platoon leader had not monitored his ammunition supply, so when he determined he should resupply, he pulled the entire platoon out of the action without coordinating with the infantry. After Marshall brought the matter up, tank platoons were subordinated to the infantry commander so that they would conserve ammunition and replenish by section instead of as a whole.[15] Marshall had not only found the system of interrogation he was looking for, but he had proved the method was significant enough in its own right to win the support of the commanders in the field.

The methodology of the group interview, as developed by Marshall, followed a basic pattern. First the historical officer researched the battle. By checking the journals for the units involved in a given engagement, he could then focus on a handful of company-size units whose efforts seem to have carried the action. Then he asked the division and regimental commanders for permission to interview the troops. Once told where and when to meet with them, he determined the starting point of the action—the first incoming or outgoing fire. With the unit assembled, the interviewer explained the reason for the interview and the two ground rules: everyone must speak up so that the entire group could hear, and all men were equal during the interview—rank meant nothing. In fact, if a soldier disagreed with his superior's testimony, it was his *duty* to make himself heard.[16]

This preamble completed, the historical officer called his first witness, often the company commander or one of the platoon leaders. As this witness mentioned the names of others, they were asked to contribute. During this early stage, the platoon leaders were asked to sketch on a blackboard, map, or sand table the terrain and dispositions the unit had been confronted with. Others were asked for futher details or corrections.

The historical officer, having gotten things going, could then turn the process over to the company commander. By paying close attention to the unfolding narrative and by prompting the commander in his questions, the historical officer could ensure that points of interest were not skimmed over. The types of questions asked were: "How did your squad go forward?" "Did it rush or did it crawl?" "What fire was delivered against you?" "What effect did casualties have on the rest of the squad?" "When you landed on the beach did you land wet or dry?" "Did you lose any equipment?" "Did you go to ground immediately?" "How did you feel when you were pinned down?"[17]

An analysis of Marshall's method involves more than the mere internal process already described. In any discussion of the technique, the time factor plays a key role. Many believe that Marshall invariably got with the troops within hours of the action. While this was sometimes the case, it would be erroneous to assume that such dispatch was common.

The time between the engagement and the interview varied depending on how long it took to get an historical officer to the unit, and when the tactical situation allowed the interviewer to get the men together. Sometimes, as on Makin Island, Marshall was literally travelling with the troops so he could begin some of the interviews immediately and continue them on the transport ships at sea. At other times, as after the Normandy invasion, Marshall had to wait weeks to interview the participants. Later, on his first trip to Korea, he usually interviewed the troops two to three weeks after an operation. On his 1953 trip, however, he was often able to debrief patrols immediately upon return from the front lines. In the Sinai in 1956 and again in 1967, Marshall arrived within a few days of the end of hostilities, so the time lag was probably a few weeks. But in Vietnam, the helicopter often enabled him to conduct an interview within hours of an engagement. The importance of the time factor lies in the fact that the longer the period between the event and the interview the less accurate memories are likely to be. Not only are details forgotten in the interim, but also a rationalization process takes place. This, of course, alters the actual train of events.

The intensity of the conflict had a great deal to do with how long it took Marshall to get to the desired units. Not only did active operations on a large scale hamper his being able to get the unit aside for the day or two necessary to conduct the interview, but also a lot of activity required the interviewer to conduct a considerable amount of research just to determine which units were key to the operation. Since there were so few historians in the field in World War II, it was impossible to interview every unit involved in an operation of any size. The historical officer had to selectively interview those units that seemed to have fought the crucial part of the engagement. In contrast, for small scale operations, like the patrolling during the relatively quiet periods in Korea in 1953 and some of the operations in Vietnam, he could focus on the unit very quickly and with little or no prior research because the operations were relatively simple.

During the course of his career, Marshall interviewed hundreds of front line units in World War II, Korea, Lebanon, Israel, and Vietnam. Exactly how many he interviewed is open to question. He suggested that in World War II alone he handled over 500 units. But that is impossible, for between 1 January 1944 and 8 May 1945 there were only 493 days. To do more than two company- or platoon-size units a day was difficult, and according to John Westover, a young combat historian who travelled extensively with Marshall in the summer and fall of 1944, they did not interview every day.

The technique itself seemed fairly simple, but as General Smith remarked, it took a certain degree of intuitive questioning and combat knowledge to employ it successfully.[18] The historical officer not only had to know the process of interviewing, but what questions to ask, whom to ask, when to delve deeper and when to move on, how to gain credibility with the unit, and how to couch the questions so as not to put a damper on the soldiers' responses. According to Forrest Pogue, another practitioner and distinguished historian in his own right, Marshall's method was tailor-made for Marshall and those with his background or skills:

> *None of us had his [Marshall's] success. He had been a young lieutenant in the first war, was called back as a lieutenant colonel, had extensive experience as a newspaperman, [and] had written a lot about the war... He could get battalion and regimental officers to bring together dozens and even hundreds of men... None of us had his rank, we lacked his skill and reputation... However, so far as we could, we tried to practice some of the lessons he had to teach.*[19]

Pogue's comments were echoed by John Westover:

> *The interviewer must pay special attention to space and time relationships. Was it probable that a man could go that distance in the time stated? In retrospect, I find that time is usually condensed. The farther from an event, the more you forget the "dead time"—when you caught your breath. My advantage over the other historians (except Marshall) was that I had had years of infantry and artillery training and had been in combat situations. Thus I was far better at judging probabilities, more inclined to question. Also, I could establish rapport. I was a combat soldier, and they soon knew it.*[20]

The directors of the historical divisions in Washington and Europe urged all historians to use Marshall's methods, but there was mixed success with it. As difficult as the method was to apply effectively, Marshall was not the only one capable of making the system work. Probably the most successful fellow practitioner was John Westover who wrote: "I watched Marshall at work and then I used it [the technique] in three wars and a variety of non-military uses. It simply cannot be beaten as a method of collecting accurate information."[21] One of the battalion commanders that Marshall showed the system to after the Normandy invasion tried it himself after the Arnheim operation. He claimed that it worked as well for him as for Marshall.[22]

Yet not everyone considered the technique a valid source of obtaining accurate information. General James M. Gavin wrote that on at least one occasion the troops resented Marshall's prying.[23] Furthermore, Marshall was not always accurate in his details.[24] A former company

27

commander, interviewed by Marshall in Vietnam, wrote that Marshall did not conduct the interview in a group environment, but rather individually with the unit's leaders. When the book *Battles in the Monsoon* came out, he claimed it was "... replete with inaccuracies—of fact, of name, of situation, of location." In addition, he said that his battalion commander, whom had been interviewed by Marshall in connection with Pork Chop Hill in the Korean War, had had a similar experience.[25]

Colonel E. M. Parker, USMA class of 1931, Rhodes scholar, and Marshall's fellow analyst with the Operations Research Office in Korea, wrote that Marshall conducted his interviews to support his preconceived ideas.[26] However, LTG H. W. O. Kinnard, one of many young officers whom Marshall interviewed in World War II, absolutely disagreed: "He would let the flow of the interview take him wherever it would lead, and not go into it with preconceived ideas."[27]

To judge for myself I conducted a spot check of three of Marshall's books, based on his notes of actual interviews. I cross-checked parts of the interview notes with the published versions of *The River and the Gauntlet, Night Drop,* and *Ambush.* I found that Marshall occasionally increased the numbers of men or the distances involved by twenty to fifty percent. Most often, however, the story followed the notes exactly. In any case, the changes were never significant in any way. For instance, in *The River and the Gauntlet* he wrote:

> *They were 129 able-bodied men when they started forward on the morning of 25 November in the great advance which was intended to reach the Yalu line and terminate the war. And though they had but recently dined on turkey and the Thanksgiving trimmings, they were in a black and resentful mood.*
>
> *By their own account, it griped them all, from Capt. William C. Wallace down to the latest replacements. Their beef was that they had been given the dirty end of the stick... It had just happened that every time Baker [Company] got forward, the enemy grew nasty, and there was subsequent fire and loss, whereas the other companies had moved along relatively unscathed.*
>
> *...Wallace deployed his Third Platoon along the base of the north slope and faced it southward. First and Second formed in an arc*

around the base of 219's western end and started upward, with First Squad, Second Platoon, serving as point and leading the other people by about 10 yards.

The time was 1015. They climbed for one quarter hour without trouble except their own hard breathing and sweat. By then the line was halfway up the hill, and the point, having lengthened its interval, was within 25 yards of the first knob.

As Pfc. Lawrence E. Smith, Jr., who was leading the squad, stopped for breath and a last look upward, a shower of twenty or more grenades came down on him. A few exploded as they hit among the rocks. Smith was struck in the thigh. Lieut. Robert A. Kjonaas, standing next to him, was wounded in the foot. These were the first shots and the first casualties in the Battle of the Chongchon; they started the "new war" at 1030 on 25 November.[28]

The record of Marshall's interview of that company, conducted at 1100 hours on December 14, 1950 states:

(Witness: Wallace) - There were ABOUT 120 MEN in the company ... One of the chief morale factors in my company at this time was that for the preceeding week or so we had been attached tactically to the 2nd Bn and we had been pushed very hard. The battalion was then advancing and we had made several contacts and had gotten into fire fights with groups of the enemy... My company had borne the brunt of the fighting. Maybe it just happened that we were always in front at the wrong time. The men all had the feeling that they should have been given some relief, since practically no other elements were engaging during this period and my men were getting more than their share of it. (All present agreed that this factor was as Wallace had stated it)... Coming to the nose of the ridge I moved 2nd and 1st platoons right up the slope to a point about half way up to the first peak. To the south of us the position was virtually unflankable, because the hill fell off so sharply. But, on the north side, the slope was somewhat gentler and I moved 3rd platoon up that way with the idea of facing the platoon northward. I was with the 2nd platoon. (Pfc. Lawrence E. Smith, Jr - I was leading 1st squad, 2nd platoon, and

> *we were serving as point just a FEW yards in advance of the others.)*
> *Witness: Wallace - I'd say 2nd platoon was half way from the*
> *base of the hill to the first knoll when we came under fire. It was*
> *automatic and rifle fire and seemed to be coming from the high*
> *ground right ahead. This happened at about 1030 hrs. (Witness:*
> *Kjonaas - I was with Smith's squad and were ABOUT 20 TO 30*
> *YDS from the first knob. Suddenly 20 or SO grenades came down*
> *on us... I got a grenade fragment in the foot and Smith was hit in*
> *the thigh...*[29]

The discrepancies in these two accounts, ranging from giving a specific figure for the distance between units to substituting the word "more" for "so" in describing the number of grenades thrown, is representative of the discrepancies I found in the other two books. In *Night Drop*, I compared four pages to the written interview; in *The River and the Gauntlet*, twenty pages; and in *Ambush*, seven pages. In each book, Marshall made minor mistakes similar to those above, but kept the sequence of events and the vast majority of the facts faithful to the testimony as he recorded it. In each case, the record was written or typed and subsequent entries were made, possibly indicating that Marshall had the witnesses read the copy and make changes as they saw fit.[30]

Of Marshall's rather unscholarly method of drawing conclusions, Westover said:

> *Keep in mind, Marshall was an intuitive thinker. He did not*
> *gather evidence, weigh it ponderously, draw tentative hypotheses,*
> *then test them. If he did, it was not in an organized manner.*
> *Usually, from "out of the blue" he stated a principle. Then he*
> *marshalled his evidence and statistics to back his concepts. Some*
> *of his statistics are subject to grave question as to source.*
>
> *What is important, though, regardless of how he established a*
> *tactical principle, it was usually sound. It was often so*
> *"self-evident" that one wonders why someone didn't think of it*
> *earlier.*[31]

Forrest Pogue went on to say of Marshall:

> *Sam's training was that of reporter. He was splendid on small level details. He had read an inordinate amount of military history, novels, adventures, memoirs, and the like. He knew some of the historians extremely well. He did not have a historian's training and, I fear, had a certain contempt for pedants who let exact facts stand in the way of a good story. At times when he was writing an article or pushing some point of doctrine, he was capable of pulling a figure out of the air and suggesting that this was based on the solid information gathered by the 200 combat historians under his command. Some of us were in total disagreement.*[32]

This was Sam Marshall the reporter. Not a true historian in the trained professional sense, Marshall would muster facts and figures in support of what were to him obvious truths. Like any historian, newsman, or writer, he selected his facts and interpreted them based on his own judgment.

Methodology and data collection notwithstanding, Marshall's efforts in the Pacific were part of an overall expansion of the Historical Branch that became evident in 1944. The number of historical teams were increased, theater programs were enlarged, and historical studies were prepared for publication. In January and February, Kemper had travelled to the European theater to investigate the historical activities and try to further the efforts of the teams in existence. While there, he visited the European Theater Historical Division under the direction of Colonel William A. Ganoe. Kemper had gone there, among other things, to promote Marshall's interview method to the historians in Europe. When he returned to Washington in March, he wrote to Marshall in the Pacific that the historians could not hope to follow the method until after they had seen it demonstrated. Since Marshall was its most successful practitioner, he was off for what Kemper termed a few months' TDY.

Indeed, Marshall was charged with two general missions to perform in Europe. He was to demonstrate the group interview method to teams in France and see as much of Europe and the Mediterranean as he could so that he could return to Washington and write a short popular history of the war.[33] Arriving in England two weeks after the invasion of France, Marshall proceeded directly to Normandy. He took Lieutenant Colonel Charles

Taylor, one of the original Branch members who was still somewhat skeptical of the group interview technique, with him. Upon reaching Normandy and finding that the First Army's historical team had not done anything to get the story of the assault on Omaha Beach, Marshall sent the team's commander, Dr. Jeremiah O'Sullivan, to the 1st Infantry Division to cover the landing, while Marshall took the airborne drop.[34]

With Colonel Taylor observing, Marshall interviewed units of the 101st. As the interview sessions progressed, Taylor, the Harvard-trained historian, retracted his objections and became one of the group interview technique's most ardent supporters.[35] Marshall returned to England with the 82nd and the 101st to continue the interviews. While there, he had three newly arrived historical officers observe his technique.[36] One of them, Lieutenant John Westover, became his constant companion for the next six months. Westover, a field artillery officer with combat experience in North Africa and Italy, and an M.A. in history from the University of Missouri in 1941, acted as Marshall's ombudsman. Together they travelled across Europe conducting group interviews and were among the first Americans to enter liberated Paris.[37]

In September 1944, Marshall wrote Kemper, now back in Washington, that he considered his work done. For nearly a year he had been laboring non-stop to get the historical program on its feet in two theaters. He had come to Europe to demonstrate his after-action group interview technique, had given the new historical officers on-the-job training in the technique, and had utilized it himself covering several operations. Marshall considered his "few weeks of TDY" at an end. But it was not time to leave. Operation Market Garden, the Allied airborne/ground assault designed to cross the Lower Rhine River in Holland, had begun. This sparked Marshall's interest and he informed Ganoe, the European Theater's Chief Historian, that he and Westover were on their way to cover the operation. Ganoe resisted, saying that Kemper intended to send Marshall to the China-Burma-India theater. Marshall told Ganoe in no uncertain words that he was going to cover Market Garden and the C-B-I would have to wait.[38] After some discussion Ganoe agreed.

While in Holland, Marshall spent his time interviewing the men from the 101st and 82nd Airborne. Upon his return six weeks later, Marshall found

Kemper in France ready to relieve Ganoe and replace him with Marshall. Marshall protested and offered another solution. He said that Ganoe was a fine man and a friend, so he would not be party to relieving him. Instead, Kemper should leave Ganoe in as the chief, while he, Marshall, took over the operation as his deputy. When the war was over, Ganoe could retire honorably.[39] Kemper agreed to the arrangement.

When the Battle of the Ardennes erupted in December 1944, Marshall was busy in Paris reorganizing Ganoe's historical headquarters. Ganoe's leadership abilities, or lack thereof, had resulted in a decentralized command and consequently productivity and respect had greatly diminished. Marshall, as deputy, tightened the chain of command in an effort to build morale and instill a feeling of unity. He immediately realized that if the historical section could cover the Ardennes operation in detail, the section would gain the respect of the high command. He demanded—and got—access to the war room. During the evening of December 18, he and Kemper made an assessment of the strategic situation and juggled the assignments of the combat historians in and near the battle area to cover as much of the action as possible.[40]

Marshall sent his protege, John Westover, and Lieutenant Joe Weber to Bastogne with orders to cover only the armored and tank destroyer aspects of the operation. Marshall promised to follow as soon as he could to handle the infantry story. As it happened, he was not able to get there until January 18, after Patton's Task Force Abrams had relieved Bastogne. By that time, Westover and Weber had already done the lion's share of the work.[41] For the next nineteen days the group labored to keep up with the fight while under fire.

When he returned to Paris, Marshall found that Ganoe had begun to act irrationally, transferring men from the historical teams of the Ninth and Fifteenth Armies to the First and Third when he had neither reason nor authority to do so. Willing to take the responsibility for his commander's actions no longer, Marshall went to Eisenhower's Services of Supply Commander, Lieutenant General John C. H. Lee, to have Ganoe relieved. Ganoe remained on the roster as Chief Historian of the European Theater, but his power remained on paper. Sam Marshall, technically still Ganoe's deputy, assumed command and control of the historical headquarters.[42]

Quite aware that the mission of the historical section could not be accomplished solely with group interviews and that he had serious shortcomings as an historian, Marshall arranged to have Major Hugh Cole promoted and transferred from Patton's Third Army to act as his deputy.[43] Marshall's next act as chief was to convince the high command that the historical division had something practical to offer the Army. He had already impressed the commanders in the Pacific that the historical officer was an invaluable source, for he had provided both the 27th and 7th Divisions with insights into both friendly and hostile combat procedures. Indeed, back in March, the commanders of these two divisions had insisted that Marshall postpone his trip to Europe for a month in order to brief them and their men on his observations and analysis. Now he had to do a similar selling job to the command structure in Europe.

Marshall chose to use his coverage of the 101st in the Battle of the Bulge as a means to justify his organization's activities. Through his contacts, Marshall sent to General Bedell Smith, Eisenhower's Chief of Staff, the story of the Bastogne operation complete with footnotes and references.[44] Smith was impressed and offered his office's assistance and support.[45]

When the war ended in Europe, Marshall's Historical Section still had a great deal of work to do, compiling and writing the account of the war. But the rapid demobilization threatened to abort the operation by sending men home regardless of the disposition of their work. Marshall fought long and hard to keep his team of historians together, going so far as to write to congressmen to put pressure in the right places.

It worked. Secretary of War Stimson cabled to General Harold R. Bull, Eisenhower's Chief of Operations:

> *If we allow officers to stay on as volunteers, provided they have essential work to do, and approve the discharge of enlisted personnel having points to come home, and their retention overseas as civilian employees with civil service rating, provided they are willing, will this satisfy your mad historian?*[46]

The "mad historian" was able to keep enough of his men on duty that the sources for the European section of *The United States Army in World War II* were compiled. Such men as Forrest Pogue, at that time a sergeant, were induced to stay on as civilians.[47]

Perhaps the most daring of all Marshall's activities during this period was the virtual kidnapping of four senior German officers from the prisoner of war compound at Oberursel. In essence, Marshall and Major Ken Hechler, who first suggested interviewing the Germans, got Generals Bayerlein, von Luttwitz, and Kokott, and Colonel von Lauchert, all major actors in the Battle of the Bulge, out of the camp without orders and flew them to Paris.[48] Working frantically with these four officers, and using his own detailed knowledge of the American side of the operation, Marshall hoped to have the interrogation completed before anyone knew what had happened to the Germans. He wanted to use the resulting view as a model for convincing the high command that the interrogation of the losers would benefit the winners.[49]

After he and Hechler finished the pilot work, as usual leaving all the administrative details of day-to-day operations to Cole, Marshall proposed to Major General Bedell Smith that the Army undertake interrogations of German prisoners of war. Smith conferred with General John C. H. Lee and decided to approve the suggestion. Rapidly Marshall put his idea into operation. Before the project was over, 250 senior German officers were interviewed.[50] From this effort came valuable information concerning how the Russians had fought, what their weaknesses were, and how the Germans had developed tactics to take advantage of these weaknesses. The Applied Studies Group, a new division of the Historical Branch in Washington wrote about 620 studies based on the interviews.[51]

While the German generals were in residence, a special committee charged with analyzing the strategy of the theater came to review the records Marshall and his men had accumulated. The committee was impressed. When Marshall went to its chairman, Lieutenant General Leonard Gerow, to get the archives sent back to the United States, Gerow agreed, though he claimed he didn't have the authority. By his order, forty-six tons of paper, all classified, were shipped to the United States.[52]

Before Marshall was released from active duty on May 3, 1946, the Chief of Staff of the Army had the first of his series of pamphlets that he had originally asked for. More importantly, the source materials for the European part of the *The United States Army in World War II* series were safely in the archives in Washington and the historical teams had begun to write drafts for that monumental work.

1. The United States Army Adjutant General, "Statement of Military Service of Samuel Lyman Atwood Marshall," October 26, 1966, p. 3. Located in the Marshall Collection, University of Texas at El Paso, hereafter referred to as the MC.

2. Marshall, *Bringing Up the Rear*, p. 54.

3. Ibid., p. 56. The younger Marshall was entirely correct in his assessment of the coverage of the war as is substantiated in Stetson Conn, *Historical Work in the United States Army 1862-1954* (Washington, D.C.: U.S. Army Center of Military History, 1980). In this work, which traces the Army's historical efforts, Conn wrote that the day the United States declared war on Germany the head of the Historical Section wrote a memorandum redefining the duties of the section, specifically stating that "no historical work of any kind on World War II was contemplated..." (p. 76). Marshall's description of events in his autobiography, including this interview with the Chief of Staff, is a dramatic portrayal of those events from his own point of view. Marshall's depiction of the meeting places him at the center. Conn's work provides a detailed picture from the point of view of those in Washington. While Marshall implied that it was his brief interview with General Marshall that made the latter aware of the state of the historical effort in the Army at the time, Conn does not refer to any such meeting and suggested that the Assistant Secretary of War John H. McCloy was a prime mover in the project of getting the war covered.

4. This came simultaneously with the Marshall reorganization of the War Department.

5. Conn, *Historical Work in the United States Army*, p. 83-4.

6. Ibid., pp. 91-2. The first in *The American Forces in Action* series was "To Bizerte with the II Corps" published in February 1944. Fourteen titles appeared before this series was discontinued.

7. Conn, *Historical Work in the United States Army*, pp. 87-8.

8. By December 1943, Kemper had two teams in the Mediterranean. By June 1944, the number of teams had risen considerably and were assigned to the field armies.

9. Marshall, *Bringing Up the Rear*, p. 62. This data, possibly the first such information obtained for World War II, formed an important part of Marshall's 1949 book, *The Soldier's Load and the Mobility of a Nation*.

10. Ibid., p. 68. Though Marshall seems to ascribe his recovery to the salt tablets, it may have been the water which had the greatest impact.

11. Ibid., p. 72.

12. Bill Davidson, "Why Our Combat Soldiers Fail to Shoot," *Collier's* (November 8, 1952). See also Marshall's 1958 speech to the 101st Airborne Division in the MC; also *Bringing Up the Rear*, p. 72.

13. Letter from Forrest Pogue to the author, August 9, 1983.

14. Letter from General Smith to Major General George V. Strong, attached to "Extracts from correspondence of Lieutenant Colonel S.L.A. Marshall, Field Representative, Historical Branch, G-2, relative to writing historical accounts of the Makin and Kwajalein operations," December 7, 1943, through January 10, 1944, found in the MC.

15. "Extracts from correspondence of Lieutenant Colonel S.L.A. Marshall, Field Representative, Historical Branch, G-2, relative to writing historical accounts of the Makin and Kwajalein operations," December 7, 1943, through January 10, 1944, found in the MC.

16. Spiller Lectures, V, December 3, 1962, p. 29. Marshall's own reply to those who thought the troops told him only what they thought he wanted to hear was that men in the presence of their comrades were less likely to overstate their own part in the battle when they knew that others would call their bluff. While still in the Pacific, Marshall deliberately had the division commander appear before the troops to give a mistaken picture of a given incident, just to see if they would dare to contradict the commander. They did.

17. S.L.A. Marshall, *Island Victory* (Washington: Zenger Publishing, 1982), p. 112.

18. Several retired generals, all of whom have experienced the technique first hand, agreed that it took great skill to conduct the interviews properly. General William R. Desobry, who was interviewed by Marshall in connection with the action of Task Force Desobry at the Battle of the Bulge, Lieutenant General A. S. Collins, Jr., who requested Marshall's help in preparing his Division for its assignment to Vietnam, and Lieutenant General H.W.O. Kinnard, G-3 of the 101st Airborne at the Bulge, all wrote that the technique was tricky, and took a keen mind. Letters from Generals Desobry, August 12, 1983; and Collins, August 9, 1983; and telephone interview with General Kinnard October 27, 1983.

19. Letter from Forrest Pogue to the author, August 9, 1983.

20. Letter from John Westover to the author, February 23, 1986.

21. Letter from John Westover to the author, August 9, 1983.

22. Spiller Lectures, V, December 3, 1962, p. 31.

23. Letter from Lieutenant General James M. Gavin to the author, August 23, 1983.

24. Reply to questionnaire from Colonel Edward M. Parker, August 12, 1983.

25. J.D. Coleman, "Ego Interferes with Marshall Memoirs," *Soldier of Fortune* (April 1981), p. 62.

26. Reply to questionnaire from Colonel Edward M. Parker, August 12, 1983.

27. Telephone interview with Lieutenant General H.W.O Kinnard, October 27, 1983.

28. S.L.A. Marshall, *The River and the Gauntlet* (New York: William Morrow and Company, 1953), pp. 18-22.

29. Text found in Marshall's field notebooks, housed in the Military History Institute, Army War College, Carlisle Barracks, Pennsylvania.

30. If Marshall allowed interviewees to come back after the interview to make corrections, he may have inadvertently introduced more error into the record. If the corrections were made immediately after the interview, then the changes may have improved the report. But if even a day or two elapsed, then the changes may reflect the rationalization process.

31. Letter from John Westover to the author, August 9, 1983.

32. Letter from Forrest Pogue to the author, August 9, 1983. Hugh Cole, head of the Third Army historical team and later Marshall's deputy, corroborated the views given by Westover and Pogue, stressing particularly strongly that with Marshall's training as a journalist, he would prefer being at the scene of the action or closeted in a room with his typewriter than do almost anything

else. Telephone interview with Cole, April 11, 1984; and letter from Cole to Marshall, May 6, 1969, found in the MC.

33. Taylor and Marshall were in England by June 10, 1944. On that date, orders were cut sending them to HQ, First U.S. Army in Normandy on June 20. It was months later that he became Deputy Theater Historian. In a secret message from General George Marshall to Eisenhower, dated October 31, 1944,: "In view of importance of Colonel Marshall's assignment to prepare ultimately a short general history of army in this war hesitate to release him for permanent assignment to one theater." On November 14, Eisenhower replied, "Recommend that Lieutenant Colonel Sam L. A. Marshall be permanently assigned with least delay this Headquarters as requested in E-57254. Believe Marshall can contribute more to Historical program as Deputy Theater Historian than any other capacity. Further recommend that he be recommended for Legion of Merit in view of outstanding service in this and Pacific Theaters." Both these messages are found in the MC.

34. Throughout *Bringing Up the Rear* it is obvious that the friends Marshall made through his interviewing the 101st Airborne remained friends throughout his life; for example, General Matthew B. Ridgway and Lieutenant Colonel (later Lieutenant General) H.W.O. Kinnard.

35. Ibid., p. 91; also Spiller Lectures, V, December 3, 1962, p. 30.

36. Marshall, *Bringing Up the Rear*, p. 94.

37. The story of how Marshall, Westover, Ernest Hemingway and six other Americans tagged along with the French 2nd Armored Division when it liberated Paris is recounted in "How Papa Liberated Paris," *The American Heritage* (April 1962), as well as in chapter 10 of Marshall's autobiography, *Bringing Up the Rear.*

38. Marshall, *Bringing Up the Rear*, p. 121.

39. Ibid., p. 122.

40. Ibid., p. 125. Most combat historians in the theater belonged to their respective corps and armies and not to the ETO Historical Division. So Marshall actually had no authority to direct these historians.

41. Ibid.

42. Ibid., pp. 130-1.

43. Ibid., p. 133.

44. This manuscript—later published as S.L.A. Marshall, *Bastogne: The First Eight Days* (Washington, D.C.: Infantry Journal Press, 1946)—Marshall bragged was his only fully footnoted publication. See the handwritten note on the cover of the copy in the Marshall Collection's shelf of special books.

45. Marshall, *Bringing Up the Rear*, p. 136.

46. Ibid., p. 145.

47. Letter from Forrest Pogue to the author, August 9, 1983. Pogue's new civilian pay grade was that of a colonel. When Bedell Smith came to Marshall in November 1945, to have someone write a short history of the Supreme Headquarters, Allied Expeditionary Forces (SHAEF), Marshall gave the job to Pogue. This eventually led to Eisenhower's personally arranging for Pogue to do the complete history of SHAEF, including giving him access to Eisenhower's papers as well as those of the Joint Chiefs of Staff and the War Department.

48. The state of affairs in Germany at the time was such that anyone could walk into one of the detention camps and walk off with a "platoon of German generals." Hugh M. Cole, telephone interview, April 11, 1984. German senior officers were being held by the British as well. Hechler did the initial leg-work, convinced Marshall of the worthiness of the project, and subsequently headed-up the group that interviewed the officers in detail. Telephone interview between Ken Hechler and the author, June 26, 1987.

49. Marshall, *Bringing Up the Rear*, p. 155.

50. Ibid., p. 158. By mid-summer 1946, over 500 generals had been interviewed. See Conn, *Historical Work in the United States Army*, p. 181.

51. Conn, *Historical Work in the United States Army*, p. 182. Eventually the Army published many of the insights derived from the interviews in a number of monographs and the DA Pamphlet 20 series.

52. Marshall, *Bringing Up the Rear,* pp. 163-4. Hugh Cole attributed the saving of these documents to Marshall's personal efforts, writing, "Sam understood the importance of [the historical records as primary sources] and moved heaven and earth at ETOUSA/SHAEF to stop the proposed shipment of the records to Liege (and a possible unknown grave)." Letter from Hugh Cole to the author, March 6, 1984.

CHAPTER THREE

THE CASE FOR *MEN AGAINST FIRE* AND *THE SOLDIER'S LOAD*

I *went where I was told to go, and I did what I was told to do, but no more. I was scared shitless just about all the time.*

James Jones

In August 1945, as the smoke cleared from the atomic explosions that blasted Hiroshima and Nagasaki, soldiers and civilians began to re-think the role of ground troops in future war. The atomic age seemed to herald a new era in warfighting. The push-button wars of yesterday's science fiction seemed an imminent reality. As science and technology invaded the battlefield, the merit and relevance of large standing armies came into question. Big bombers, rockets, and sophisticated nuclear weaponry appeared to be a force potent enough to replace the millions of men kept under arms.

Above the din, there were a few voices stridently asserting that war would always require well-trained ground troops. Among the voices was that of Sam Marshall. Recently returned to a civilian job as an editor for the *Detroit News*, Marshall found that his experiences in two world wars did not support the popular view advocating reliance on high technology and the nuclear arsenal. He was very much a spokesman for the common soldier. With the encouragement of some of his friends, his writing took on a new slant. No longer would he write about the strategies of mechanized war, but rather about the nature of man in battle. All of this was driven by the inherent belief that the infantry soldier would still determine the course of warfare.

In the May 1947 issue of the *Infantry Journal*, Marshall began a series of articles entitled "Battle Command in Future War." The articles were actually the debut of his book, *Men Against Fire*, which was to be published later in the year. Hailed as one of the most important books to come out of World War II, *Men Against Fire* was an analysis of infantry combat performance that Marshall had observed and chronicled during World War II. His expressed purpose was to enlighten leadership to the reality of the modern battlefield and speed implementation of corrective training. In doing so, he fought against the prevailing trust in strategic atomic forces, the new toys of technology.

Marshall examined several areas in his analysis of the nature of war at the soldiers' level. His experiences indicated to him that contrary to popular belief, success in battle often depended on an amazingly small amount of fire by just a few men, delivered at just the right time, in just the right place. As examples of this he cited the efforts of a unit on Omaha Beach and of twelve men at the Bourcy roadblock north of Bastogne. According to Marshall, it was the efforts of only forty-seven men that saved the day at Omaha.[1] At Bourcy, twelve infantrymen, having fired into advance elements of the German 2nd Panzer Division, had fallen back to another position. But their fire had convinced the German regimental commander that he was being engaged by superior forces. When German Corps headquarters heard the report, it ordered the 2nd Panzer Division to swing away, and, in so doing, the Germans lost the race to Bastogne.[2]

Men Against Fire was much more than a compilation of war stories, however. Marshall had noticed patterns of human behavior on the battlefields of the two world wars. He observed two startling and interrelated phenomena. First, troops fighting the second were much quieter than the doughboys of World War I. Second, his interviews of World War II had brought to the fore a startling revelation—most riflemen didn't fire their weapons even when threatened with death. Correcting the two deficiencies became the major focus of *Men Against Fire.* In 1947 he wrote:

> *What we need in battle is more and better fire.*
>
> *What we need to seek in training are any and all means by which we can increase the ratio of effective fire when we have to go to war.*[3]

One of the means of increasing effective fire, Marshall suggested, was to increase communication. He strongly believed that fire and person-to-person communication were the twin essentials of successful minor tactics.[4] Marshall urged that the Army investigate its training in regard to information flow. By improving communication, the Army would increase the likelihood that a man would stand his ground, that he would fire, that he would exercise initiative, and that a unit would respond to crises with unity of action.

By themselves, these proposals do not seem extraordinary. Indeed, Marshall himself would probably have said they were just common sense. But the fact is that until he began to stress them and to offer concrete proof that proper training was not being conducted, many military men relied on antiquated, inappropriate methods to achieve tactical success. Marshall concluded that even the most experienced leaders virtually ignored the realities of human nature, and when figuring how to increase their chances of success in battle looked only at the "geometry of the problem."[5]

Marshall noted that service schools had taught soldiers to consider the deployment and positioning of weapons as the commander's most crucial tactical consideration. That is, an officer should first examine the terrain to determine where he could best create interlocking bands of fire. The physical characteristics of the weapons and the ground on which they were deployed were thought to constitute the crucial planning factor. But Marshall thought otherwise:

> *The heart of the matter is to relate the man to his fellow soldier as he will find him on the field of combat, to condition him to human nature as he will learn to depend on it when the ground offers him no comfort and his weapons fail.*[6]

Additionally, officers had applied the adage that discipline makes a soldier and that the road to discipline is through drill and repetition. Marshall considered this putting the cart before the horse. He maintained that discipline came from morale, not the other way around.[7] The cause of poor training, according to Marshall, was the application of eighteenth-century principles of discipline to modern warfare. The advances in weaponry demanded a change in training and discipline which had not been realized.[8] Although everyone was aware that personal initiative was crucial in modern war, automatic response was still the main goal of training, as it had been for centuries. Leaders thus faced a training challenge—how to reconcile the need for individual initiative with the tradition of discipline to orders.[9] Tactically, the American soldier had been encouraged to think creatively as a person, but not encouraged to act or speak as a team member.[10] Participation in combat could be increased, it was believed, by increasing a soldier's confidence in his weapon or his enjoyment of firing it.[11]

What Marshall noted in *Men Against Fire*, however, was that most troops did not enjoy firing at all. A short battle narrative is illustrative.

> *To return to the beginning of the Makin Island fight, which was part of the Gilbert Islands invasion in November, 1943, one battalion of the 165th Infantry Regiment was stoutly engaged all along the front of its defensive perimeter throughout the third night. The enemy, crazed with sake, began a series of Banzai charges at dusk, and the pressure thereafter was almost unremitting until dawn came. The frontal gun positions were all directly assaulted with sword and bayonet. Most of the killing took place at less than a ten-yard interval. Half of the American guns were knocked out and approximately half of the occupants of the forward foxholes were either killed or wounded. Every position was ringed with enemy dead.*
>
> *When morning brought the assurance that the defensive position had weathered the storm and the enemy had been beaten back by superior fire, it seemed certain to those of us that were close enough to it to appraise the action that all concerned must have acted with utmost boldness. For it was clear that the whole battalion was alive*

to the danger and that despite its superior numbers it had succeeded by none too wide a margin. We began the investigation to determine how many of our men had fought with their weapons. It was an exhaustive search, man by man and gun crew by gun crew, each man being asked exactly what he had done.

Yet making allowances for the dead, we could identify only 36 men as having fired at the enemy with all weapons. [An infantry company typically had approximately 200 soldiers; a battalion about four times as many.]

The really active firers were usually in small groups working together. There were some men in the positions directly under attack who did not fire at all or attempt to use a weapon even when the position was being overrun. The majority of the active firers used several weapons; if the machine gun went out, they picked up a rifle; when they ran out of rifle ammunition they used grenades. But there were other witnesses who testified that they had seen clear targets and still did not fire.[12]

As Marshall found when he was transferred to Europe, the pattern remained essentially the same. Although the geography and pace of combat was different, in both theaters he used the same method of identifying the firers, and got similar results:

In an average experienced infantry company in an average stern day's action, the number engaging with any and all weapons was approximately 15 per cent of total strength. In the most aggressive infantry companies, under the most intense local pressure, the figure rarely rose above 25 per cent of total strength from the opening to the close of action.

Now maybe I should clarify the matter still further. I do not mean to say that throughout an engagement, the average company maintained fire with an average of 15 per cent of its weapons. If that were it, there would be no problem, for such a rate of fire would necessarily mean great volume during the height of an assault.

The thing is simply this, that out of an average one hundred men along the line of fire during the period of an encounter, only fifteen men on the average would take any part with the weapons.

45

This was true whether the action was spread over a day, or two days, or three. The prolonging of the engagement did not add appreciably to the numbers.

Moreover, men did not have to maintain fire to be counted among the active firers. If he had so much as fired a rifle once or twice, though not aiming it at anything in particlular, or lobbed a grenade in the direction of the enemy, he was scored on the positive side. Usually the men with heavier weapons, such as the BAR, flamethrower or bazooka, gave a pretty good account of themselves, which of course is just another way of saying that the majority of men who were present and armed but would not fight were riflemen.[13]

Marshall would not classify those who stayed but did not fight as cowards or as useless baggage in combat. "They did not shirk the final risk of battle. They were not malingerers. They did not hold back from the danger point. They were there to be killed if the enemy fire searched and found them."[14]

But why would they stay and yet not fight? Marshall observed that though a rifleman hesitated to expose himself by firing his weapon, he was even more fearful of losing face in the eyes of his comrades. Personal honor and social pressure were the bases of battle discipline. Should the soldier flee, he would not only chance exposure to the enemy, but, more importantly, his comrades would observe his flight and consider him a coward—a judgment which could not be escaped even upon returning to a safe place.[15] Furthermore, soldiers who advanced but did not fire still made an important contribution. Passive soldiers did not detract from the effectiveness of the active firers, because their mere presence provided moral support to the firers.[16]

Marshall observed another important reaction to combat which had hitherto been overlooked. When investigating the cause of the forty-five to sixty minute halt which an advancing line inevitably experienced upon receiving fire, Marshall reported that it was the act of diving for cover that severed all sense of unity. Since it took time to restore low-level communication and to reintegrate the unit, the delay precluded any further movement. The men would not advance as long as they felt isolated.

Marshall suggested that to reduce the reintegration time, the commander must train the small unit leaders to re-establish contact with their men immediately upon hitting the ground.[17] Assurance of mutual support was absolutely necessary to regain momentum.

Marshall offered several specific explanations for a man's failure in combat, such as unrealistic expectations of battle, the fear of killing a living creature, unexpected rearward movement, cultural inhibitions, and difficult weather. All of these ultimately tied into communication, or more accurately, the lack thereof, which engendered feelings of isolation and fear. The American soldier had been taught by his family, his school, and his religion that aggression and killing were wrong. Obviously, this hindered him in combat. His reluctance to fire was caused by an emotional, unconscious restraint, not an intellectual one. Psychiatrists investigating combat fatigue cases found that, "Fear of killing, rather than of being killed, was the most common cause of battle failure in the individual, and that fear of failure ran a strong second."[18] If a soldier could avoid it, he would not kill.

Marshall proposed that training was not realistic. A soldier experienced one thing in training and quite another in combat. The sudden realization that his perception of combat was an illusion paralyzed him. A recruit, thinking about battle, expected that when danger came, he would be comforted by the presence of other members of the team, other units, and the very power of the Army. The expectation arose from all his precombat experiences. In training, on the parade field, and during exercises he saw people around him constantly. He felt he was always being watched. Furthermore, the training films, the dayroom pictures, and Hollywood movies always depicted the enemy as clear and visible. The problem with the image was that it was misleading. The harshest thing about a battlefield was not that it was full of charging enemy hordes, but that it was empty with little or no action most of the time. Firing was only occasional, yet danger was ever-present. When combat came, troops were not able to see very far and they felt more alone than ever before.[19]

Marshall noted that some soldiers reacted to enemy fire by returning fire blindly, for they did not see any clear targets; or timidly, for they expected someone to chide them for wasting ammunition. But most men did nothing; some because they were confused about the unexpected situation and awaited orders, others because they were paralyzed with fear and could not think. Nor were junior leaders immune to these apprehensions, often losing self-confidence with every moment of inaction. They hesitated to give a clear order and so the problem intensified. "Could one clear commanding voice be raised, ... [the men] would obey, or at least the stonger characters would do so and the weaker would begin to take heart because something is being done."[20] So, Marshall urged, the problem of reluctance to fire should be addressed in training rather than expecting the leader to initiate corrective action on the battlefield. Corrective action on the battlefield required extreme measures and was unlikely to bring about sustained results. For example, on the night of 10 June 1944, along the Carentan Causeway in Normandy, a battalion of airborne infantry was strung out in the open, exposed to rifle fire from Germans barely 300-700 yards away. The battalion commander, Lieutenant Colonel Robert G. Cole, earned the Congressional Medal of Honor for his attempts to get his men to fire. He moved constantly up and down the line, exhorting his men. At an after-action interview in front of his battalion, Cole said:

> *I found no way to make them continue fire. Not one man in twenty-five voluntarily used his weapon. There was no cover; they could not dig in. Therefore their only protection was to continue a fire which would make the enemy keep his head down. They had been taught this principle in training. They all knew it very well. But they could not force themselves to act upon it. When I ordered the men around me to fire, they did so. But the moment I passed on, they quit. I walked up and down the line yelling, "God damn it! Start shooting!" But it did little good. They fired only while I watched them or while some other officer stood over them.[21]*

Marshall observed the major cause of tactical mishap was the lack of information. Communication, both lateral and vertical, was crucial to morale, discipline, and performance. Marshall maintained that all men should be kept informed of the strengths and intentions of adjacent units. Otherwise, when the firing began, a soldier assumed he was unsupported and would be more likely to retreat or panic if put under pressure. Knowing that there were friendlies nearby boosted morale and hence discipline.

48

But in order for the soldier to know the strengths and intentions of friendly forces, to include his own, his leaders must seek out this information and disseminate it. As Marshall noted, lack of adequate communication spawned feelings of isolation and fear. Often this was manifested by the most threatening of battlefield occurrences, the panicked retreat. And panic is the operative word here. Retreat is a legitimate tactical and strategic maneuver. Add panic to this otherwise natural movement and one is left with a condition that, if unchecked, can tear the heart out of any body of troops. Marshall investigated several panics of World War II and found that in each case the panic could have been avoided merely by informing everyone in the area of an intended rearward movement.[22] For example, on June 12, 1944, during the fight for the Carentan Causeway, a sergeant, suddenly wounded, headed for the aid station without telling his squad where he was going. The squad and soon the whole line withdrew, thinking that orders had been given to that effect.[23] Having identified some causes of tactical disintegration, Marshall presented possible solutions. "It is my belief that a system of man-to-man control on the battlefield is our great need in tactics and ... it is fully attainable."[24] The solutions were to be found in the differences between combat and training. In training, safety was stressed to the point that movement under fire was unrealistically conducted. Second, in training situations, a soldier did not have a man as his target. Firing was conducted on a known-distance range cleared of any distractions other than the sound of other men's weapons—no shrubs, no dead space, no uncertainties of any sort. Third, whereas in training a soldier was closely watched and was motivated by the desire to impress his superiors, in combat he was on his own, the chief pressure to remain alive. What one does to survive may be drastically different than what one does to make a favorable impression.

An army must ensure that training is as realistic as possible to prepare soldiers for what they will experience on the battlefield. Since fear is a permanent condition of combat, and since uncontrolled fear is the real enemy, the better the soldier understands and anticipates the dangers and distractions of the battlefield, the more likely he is to control his fear, and from there improve the chances of tactical success.[25]

What Marshall stressed now seems obvious. The American soldier must be trained from the very beginning that he must talk with others. Conversation dispels the loneliness of the battlefield and facilitates understanding of the conditions of war. Only if troops and leaders are trained that combat inevitably results in disorder will they be able to establish order when confronted with unexpected crises.

> *How many times on the field of battle one sees a young commander unnecessarily dismayed and shaken because the reality is so unlike what he had envisaged! Viewing the chaos, the litter and the inaction, he thinks them the tokens of defeat because his nerve has not been steeled or his eye trained to look for the signs of order and of progress amid the confusion.*[26]

Leaders must be trained to keep this fear in check. Marshall suggested several specific points designed to break the relationship between fire and fear. Leaders need to be aware that many men fire only when given a specific order to do so. They should then take note of who is unwilling to fire and should attempt to give them special attention.[27] When the leader gives an order, he must ensure that it is clear and forceful, for "... an order only half heard becomes a convenient excuse for noncompliance."[28] The soldier must furthermore be trained to exercise concentric initiative rather than eccentric initiative, that is, initiative towards group—not individual—action. To do this, he must be trained to speak to his comrades rather than to remain silent in a crisis.

Not only must lateral communications improve, but so must vertical communication. Often, Marshall found, a commander found a novel, effective way of overcoming a problem but did not pass his solution on to others outside his unit. The cause was not selfishness or modesty, but his training. He was trained to think not how he could help others, but how others could help him. Marshall asserted that the Army must foster the awareness that everyone has something valuable to contribute.[29]

To overcome the soldier's learned reluctance to kill, Marshall urged a new approach to marksmanship training. Soldiers should be trained to fire at non-personnel targets such as bushes and windows rather than solely the traditional bulls-eyes. Training should teach men to mass fire on command against targets like river embankments, the roots of trees at the edge of a

50

forest, or on hillcrests. By training both the leaders and the soldiers in the proper use of men on the battlefield, the Army could increase its fire ratio.

For those who showed no initiative after the first fire fight, Marshall suggested that the leader assign them to a gun crew.

> *...There, the group will keep them going. Men working in groups or in teams do not have the same tendency to default on fire as do single riflemen. This is such a well-fixed principle in human nature that one very rarely sees a gun go out of action simply because the opposing fire is too close.*[30]

An alternative solution for handling the unwilling firers, according to Marshall, was to put them on the heavier single-man weapons. Such assignments allowed them the opportunity to show others that they deserved more respect than they had been getting.[31] As for self-starters, Marshall noted that they should not be wasted on rear area duties or continuously concentrated on hazardous duties like outposts and patrols. No matter what tasks they were given, self-starters should be allowed as much freedom of action as possible. Over-supervision would ruin them.[32]

These were the major conclusions Marshall brought out in *Men Against Fire*. The response to them was immediate. Members of the Army Ground Forces training division, to include the G-3, chief of staff, and commanding general, were highly enthusiastic about Marshall's findings and the implications they held for the U.S. Army.[33] Almost overnight *Men Against Fire* elevated Marshall's reputation from that of civilian journalist turned historian to astute military analyst.

In December 1947, only months after *Men Against Fire* was published, the commanding generals of the First, Second, Third, and Sixth Armies received the Revised Program of Instruction to go into effect in January 1948. *Men Against Fire* was used as a reference for several blocks of instruction including "Introduction to Leadership" and "Combat Leadership."[34] In 1949, the Command and General Staff College published a text entitled *Military Psychology* which included *Men Against Fire* in its bibliography.[35] In January 1950, The Engineer School published the text *Military Leadership*, and sent Marshall a copy saying:

> *We have used some of your material in this text, particularly that contained in your fine book, "Men Against Fire." In the class*

> *discussions which are based on this text material, we are also using*
> *your book for illustrations, case histories, and practical application*
> *of the text material.*[36]

Also in 1950, the Army General School published *Leadership for the Company Officer*, giving as one of its ten recommended readings, *Men Against Fire.*[37]

Marshall's reputation was not confined to members of the United States Army. His influence travelled overseas as well. In 1948, Colonel W. T. Campbell of the British Joint Services Mission wrote Marshall that the War Office had asked him to find out more about the behavior of the nonfirer.[38] In January 1949, Major J. P. Searight, of the War Office, asked Marshall if *Men Against Fire* was going to be published in Britain, as he wanted to review it in the *British Army Journal*. "It might interest you to know that I have lent my copy of it to General Sir Brian Horrocks, who is at this moment engaged in writing our new manual on training."[39] In addition to foreign and high level correspondence, Marshall received letters from junior officers indicating that he had explained for them incidents and reactions that they had experienced in World War II but had not understood at the time.[40]

Men Against Fire caught the attention of the military with the startling proposal that only fifteen percent of American infantry soldiers in World War II fired their weapons in any given combat situation. Not an impressive statistic on its own, and easily taken out of context, it nonetheless called attention to the relationship between fear and America's fighting force. Marshall noted that, "Fear is ever present, but it is uncontrolled fear that is the enemy of successful operation, and the control of fear depends upon the extent to which all dangers and distractions may be correctly anticipated and therefore understood."[41] Marshall's purpose in writing *Men Against Fire* had been to educate the military mind on the realities of the battlefield, as he had observed them, and provide avenues for improvement in training and doctrine. To a great extent this effort was continued in his second major publication, *The Soldier's Load*. This work also examined fear, but in its interactive relationship with fatigue.

Marshall's experiences in World War I and II, including the testimony of the men he interviewed, led him to think that fear and fatigue were somehow related. When on Makin he found that salt tablets and water restored his self-control, he realized that the abject cowardice he felt was caused by fatigue or dehydration or some other physiological condition. Just what it was, he could not identify. It took the testimony of the soldiers who landed on Omaha Beach to give him the corroboration he needed.

Marshall's after-action interviews of E Company, 16th Infantry on the Omaha Beach landings rekindled memories of shock, inertia, and elevated casualties.[42] The survivors had agreed that most men had advanced at the pace of the incoming tide—they were physically unable to move any faster. "The Company lost more men to the water behind it than to the fire from in front, it required one hour to cross 250 yards of beach."[43] Likewise, Company M, 116th Infantry, made it across the beach in ten minutes—but crawling. They were too weak to take more than a few steps at a time. Staff Sergeant Thomas Turner provided Marshall with a crucial key to understanding when he stated, "Under fire we learned what we had never been told—that fear and fatigue are about the same in their effect on an advance."[44]

Recalling a discussion with his friend J.F.C. Fuller in June 1944, Marshall dug up an obscure British Army booklet. In the 1920s the Hygiene Advisory Committee of the British Army had studied the history of how soldiers have been loaded down through the centuries. Its report, *The Load Carried by the Soldier*, reinforced Marshall's ideas on the subject.[45] The pamphlet noted that with few exceptions commanders have always expected their men to carry from fifty-five to eighty pounds into battle. The committee reached an absolute conclusion "... that NOT IN EXCESS OF FORTY TO FORTY-FIVE POUNDS was a tolerable load for an average-sized man on a road march."[46] More specifically, it stated that for training purposes, the optimum load, including clothing and personal belongings, was one-third of the soldier's body weight. Greater weights caused the cost of carrying the load to rise disproportionately to the actual increment of weight.

Marshall next consulted the results of a series of tests conducted by the German Army some fifty years prior. The tests were designed to measure the effect on soldiers of various loads under varying temperatures. The study concluded that the absolute limit in combat should not exceed forty-eight pounds per man.[47] Marshall suggested that, "rations and ammunition should be specified only in the amounts which reason and experience tell us the soldier is likely to expend in one day. Beyond that, everything should be committed to first line transport."[48] He emphasized this because in World War II, American troops hit the beaches with three days' rations on their backs, weighing approximately nine pounds, even though shipments of food were coming ashore immediately behind them. Marshall recommended one-third of a ration be shipped off with the troops as "we learned by actual survey on the battlefield that only some three per cent of the men along the combat line touched any food at all in the first day's fighting. And that water consumption was only a fifth of what it became on the second day and thereafter." [49]

As for ammunition, Marshall referred to his notes of interviews with the 82nd and 101st Airborne Divisions and concluded that the soldier did not need as much as was commonly believed.

> *The belief that it is good for his battle morale ... is a psychological fallacy... The willing fighter will spend his last round if convinced that the tactical situation requires it. And he will then look around to see where he can get some more ammunition.*[50]

As for the contention that he might run out of ammunition at a critical time, Marshall cited three reasons why, in modern combat, soldiers were not likely to lack the means of fire. First, supply vehicles were mechanized thus making expedient resupply possible. Second, those few firers could always get ammunition from the dead and from those who would not fire. And third, a given unit was seldom hit equally along its front, thereby enabling it to conduct internal resupply.

Although two hundred rounds of ammunition per man had been the standard load from the mid-nineteenth century, in World War II the American soldier in the Pacific carried eighty rounds and five to eight grenades. Marshall's interview notes indicated that less than six percent of combat soldiers used grenades at all, and about the same number used all eighty rounds.[51] Since eight grenades weighed over ten pounds, cutting back on them alone would represent a considerable reduction.

With all this data, Marshall wrote another series of articles for *The Infantry Journal* which later became the book *The Soldier's Load and the Mobility of a Nation*. In the preface to the 1965 edition he said:

> *The basic theme is elementary and should be beyond argument: no logistical system is sound unless its first principle is enlightened conservation of the power of the individual fighter.*
>
> *The secondary theme ... is that sustained fear in the male individual is as degenerative as prolonged fatigue and exhausts body energy no less.*[52]

According to Marshall, the British and German studies, while admirable as far as they went, failed to consider the role of the soldier as being different from that of a beast of burden. A soldier was not a pack animal but a warrior. Therefore,

> *...the logistical limits of the human carrier should not be measured in terms of how much cargo he can haul without permanent injury to bone and muscle, but of what he can endure without critical, and not more than temporary impairment of his mental and moral powers...*[53]

Commanders at all levels must keep the soldier's mental as well as physical limitations in mind when conducting operations.

But what exactly was the connection between fear and fatigue? Put simply, "Tired men take fright more easily [and] frightened men swiftly tire."[54] There was a definite reciprocal relationship. Once a man was overloaded, he became tired. Once tired, he became more prone to fear. Once fearful, he lost strength, and the cycle continued.

Marshall incorporated the findings of the earlier German and British studies, which advocated using 1/3 of body weight as the maximum training load, and reduced the combat load to 4/5 of the training load. Since according to official figures, the average American soldier weighed 153.6 pounds, the optimum training load was figured at fifty-one pounds. According to Marshall, given standard equipment weights, fifty-one pounds would not only give the soldier his combat essentials but also allow him to carry two blankets and a raincoat. For combat, Marshall cautioned that the soldier should carry no more than forty pounds. Again, using his own judgment, he determined that allowing 11.03 pounds for the uniform itself, plus two grenades, two belts of M-1 ammunition, one K ration, and other minor essentials, the soldiers' combat load could be kept at 39.94 pounds.[55]

So Marshall was offering a solution to the complex problem of fear, fatigue, and battle performance. A major part of the solution required that leaders as well as soldiers be convinced that the problem was met and overcome. The first step was explaining the problem simply, as he had done in *The Soldier's Load:*

> *Up to the zone where men come under fire, ninety percent of the problem of movement can be solved with the horsepower of our machines. From that line forward, ninety per cent of success depends on will power... Whether [a soldier] moves forward or hesitates in the moment when his life is at stake is almost wholly dependent on how well he has been led.*[56]

Leaders must have "... the courage to believe that the soldier with only five clips in his pocket but spring in his gait is tenfold stronger than the man who is foundered under the weight of ammunition he will never use." The Army must teach the soldier to believe "that a toughened back and strong legs will give him his main chance for survival, but at the same time [the Army must teach] the command and staff to treat those firm muscles as the Army's most precious combat assets."[57]

How did senior officers react to Marshall's conclusions and proposals? In Marshall's own words:

> *The paper which I did three years ago on the load of the soldier has finally scored a total success at the decisive point. The Army accepted it almost immediately in theory and a complete action program is now coming of it. The load has been re-standardized at the figures which I set. All basic equipment other than arms is now being remodelled so that it will come within the formula, new logistical safeguards are being set up and staff procedures are being refined so that the basic requirements will not be overridden in times of extraordinary pressure.*[58]

Was Marshall right? Completely. Not only did General Devers, Chief of Army Field Forces, ask Marshall to send him a copy of his study of the problem in May 1949, but he also invited him to testify before the newly appointed Army Equipment Board.[59] Marshall did so that July. It is not correct to say, however, that Marshall was the first one to notice the problem of overloading. According to General Devers, the subject was an important one at the 1946 Infantry Conference. Little had been done, however. According to the report of the Quartermaster Climatic Research Laboratory, one of the two official organizations which began research into the subject, Marshall's publicity made the research possible. Before he came forth with *The Soldier's Load*, overloading remained a topic of discussion, but one which everyone had his own opinion on and which suffered from lack of hard evidence. Marshall's efforts goaded the military to dedicate resources toward studying the problem.[60] Out of the efforts of the Quartermaster's research and that of the Army Field Forces Board, new equipment was designed and tested. For the first time, equipment was designed to be comfortable, riding lower on the body. "Prior to that, uniforms were designed for appearance, not so much for functional purpose."[61] In 1956, Major General T.L. Sherburne, Director of Personnel Operations, wrote:

> *I appreciated very much a copy of "The Soldier's Load and the Mobility of a Nation." I have read through it already and am particularly interested in your prescription for accouterments of the individual soldier. I am trying to get Dep Log [the Deputy Chief of Staff for Logistics] to design a water-proof warm, light envelope that men can carry in mean weather.*[62]

In the immediate post-war period, Marshall's star was definitely rising. The letters he received from people who read his books and articles clearly indicated his thinking had stirred the minds of many. In the four years following his release from active duty, he was called back forty-seven times for various lengths of time, and for various reasons. Sometimes he contributed to national policy for the military on matters far removed from the battlefield, "... policy that led to NATO, the Berlin airlift, and Tito's problems with the Soviets."[63] Equally important, he was asked to speak at service schools—a practice which he kept up throughout his remaining years.

1. S.L.A. Marshall, *Men Against Fire* (Gloucester, Mass.: Peter Smith, 1978), p. 11.

2. Ibid., p. 69.

3. Ibid., pp. 22-23.

4. Ibid., p. 135.

5. Ibid., p. 51.

6. Ibid., p. 38.

7. Ibid., pp. 158-9.

8. Ibid., p. 12.

9. Ibid., p. 40.

10. Ibid., p. 127.

11. Ibid., p. 76.

12. Ibid., pp. 55-6.

13. Ibid., pp. 56-7. This passage is the most controversial, most quoted, and most misunderstood part of all Marshall's writings. But oddly enough, a study conducted during World War II by an independent agency in large part supported Marshall. See Samuel A. Stouffer, *The American Soldier*, Vol. II, *Combat and its Aftermath* (Princeton: Princeton University Press, 1949), p. 192.

14. Ibid., p. 59. The idea of "Killers, Fillers, and Fodder" is well expressed by Colonel Thomas A. Horner in his article by that name in the September 1982 issue of *Parameters*, the Journal of the U.S. Army War College, pages 27-34.

15. Marshall, *Men Against Fire*, p. 149.

16. Ibid., p. 65.

17. Ibid., p. 130. Because of *Men Against Fire*, the Army dropped the one-man foxhole in favor of a two-man foxhole. See letter from General William E. DePuy, former commander of the U.S. Army Training and Doctrine Command, to the author, February 14, 1984.

18. Marshall, *Men Against Fire*, p. 78.

19. Marshall, *Men Against Fire*, p. 45.

20. Ibid., pp. 48-9.

21. Marshall, *Men Against Fire*, p. 72. This occurred in one of the most vaunted units of World War II, the 101st Airborne Division. Ultimately Cole got frustrated with the situation, ordered his men to fix bayonets, and charged the enemy. For this action, he received the Medal of Honor.

22. Ibid., pp. 145-6.

23. Ibid., p. 150.

24. Ibid., p. 39.

25. Ibid., p. 37.

26. Ibid., p. 181.

27. Ibid., p. 82.

28. Ibid., p. 139.

29. Ibid., pp. 40-1.

30. Ibid., pp. 75-6.

31. Ibid., p. 76. The idea that infantrymen armed with BARs were generally more active than those with only rifles led Marshall to suggest that the squad (approximately twelve men) be divided into two teams, each formed around an automatic rifle. In time, this suggestion was adopted. See S.L.A. Marshall, "Commentary on Infantry Operations and Weapons Usage in Korea; Winter of 1950-51", published by the Johns Hopkins University, Operations Research Office, Report No. ORO-R-13, October 27, 1951, pp. 53-4.

32. Marshall, *Men Against Fire,* pp. 79-80.

33. Letters from B.F. Purdue, Colonel, Army Ground Forces Operations and Training Officer (G-3) to Marshall, September 17, 1947, and October 1, 1947, both in the MC. Also, letter from General Jacob L. Devers, Commanding General, Army Ground Forces, to Marshall, October 1, 1947, also in the MC.

34. This publication found in the MC.

35. Found in the MC.

36. Letter from Colonel Henning Linden, Infantry, Chief of the Military Leadership Department, January 31, 1950, MC.

37. *Leadership for the Company Officer,* Army General School Special Text Number 1, Revised, Fort Riley, Kansas, 1950. The Army General School was established as the Ground General School in 1946. It was renamed the Army General School in 1950 and disestablished in 1955.

38. Letter from W.T. Campbell, Colonel, SDW&T (Infantry/Air), British Joint Services Mission, January 19, 1948, found in the MC.

39. Letter from Major Searight, the War Office, Whitehall, London, January 29, 1949, MC.

40. For example, Captain Steve W. Mulkey, Infantry, USMA Class of 1944, wrote Marshall that *Men Against Fire* validated his personal experiences in the European Theater. The letter is dated February 1949 and can be found in the MC.

41. Marshall, *Men Against Fire,* p. 37.

42. S.L.A. Marshall, *The Soldier's Load and the Mobility of a Nation* (Quantico, Va.: The Marine Corps Association, 1980), p. 38.

43. Ibid., pp. 39-40.

44. Ibid., p. 44.

45. N.V. Lothian, Major, Medical Corps, Royal Army Medical Corps, *The Load Carried by the Soldier,* Army School of Hygiene, Army Hygiene Advisory Committee Report No. 1 (London: John Bale, 1918), found in the MC.

46. Marshall, *The Soldier's Load,* pp. 25-6.

47. Ibid., pp. 48-9.

48. Ibid., p. 57.

49. Ibid., p. 10.

50. Ibid., p. 18.

51. Ibid., pp. 12-13.

52. Ibid., p. iii.

59

53. Ibid., p. 8.

54. Ibid., p. 46.

55. Ibid., pp. 71-3. Marshall further clarified his ideas on the load when, during the Korean War, he wrote, "Commentary on Infantry Operations and Weapons Usage in Korea." In this report, he described how his predictions about overburdening the soldier would result in great waste; how the soldiers determined on their own what their maximum limit was—and it was close to his own estimate of 38-45 pounds; and how stress on all, including staffs, was exacerbated by the leadership's not knowing the limits of its men. See S.L.A. Marshall, "Commentary on Infantry Operations and Weapons Usage in Korea; Winter of 1950-51," published by the Johns Hopkins University, Operations Research Office, Report No. ORO-R-13, October 27, 1951, pp. 29-50.

56. Marshall, *The Soldier's Load*, p. 75.

57. Ibid., p. 52. Interestingly enough, Marshall noticed that the Army may have over-applied his admonition to keep the soldier's burden to a minimum. After visiting the 1st Airborne Battle Group in Lebanon in 1958, Marshall wrote an article, "Amid Doves and Olive Branches," for *The Combat Forces Journal*. In this article, he said that while the troops trained well and reacted well under very trying conditions, they had been outloaded too light. They lacked essentials; they carried only one change of socks and underwear. See the October 1958 edition, p. 20.

58. Letter from Marshall to B.H. Liddell Hart, August 19, 1952, MC.

59. Letter from General Jacob Devers to Marshall, May 26, 1949, MC.

60. Farrington Daniels, Jr., *Physiology of Load Carrying*, Quartermaster Research Laboratory, Environmental Research Branch, Quartermaster Research and Development Command, Report No. 203 (March 1953), p. 1.

61. Lieutenant General William J. McCaffrey, personal interview, August 18, 1983. Marshall's contention that the Army took immediate action is borne out in an article in *The Army Times* on September 3, 1949. In an article in the *Combat Forces Journal*, a member of the Army Field Forces Board No. 3 wrote that in 1950, the board recommended the maximum weights the soldier would be required to carry. They were virtually identical to what Marshall had suggested. See Major Richard T. Matthews, "The Load of the Individual Soldier," *Combat Forces Journal* (October 1952): 12ff.

62. Letter from Major General T.L. Sherburne to Marshall, March 30, 1956, MC.

63. Marshall, *Bringing Up the Rear*, p. 167. Also see the orders in the files of the Marshall Collection. Although they do not specify the purpose of any given assignment, the orders do indicate that Marshall was called up for duty with not only service schools, but also the Historical Division and the Office of the Chief of Information.

CHAPTER FOUR

EARLY IMPACT OF *MEN AGAINST FIRE*

...[There struggled]
Sisyphus, whose task was to roll a huge stone up a hill-top, but when the steep was well-nigh gained, the rock, repulsed by some sudden force, rushed again headlong down to the plain. Again he toiled at it, while sweat bathed all his weary limbs, but all to no effect.

Bullfinch's Mythology

Having committed himself to his theories of fire and fatigue in the late 1940s, and thereby stirring up a great deal of interest and controversy, Marshall spent the rest of his life promoting and defending those theories. Although he had impressed some very influential people, Marshall's ideas would not live a life of their own. He thought they were self-evident, but, as he was to find out, reforming a large organization with a strong sense of tradition, even with the help of its leaders, was no simple task.

Before he died in 1977, Marshall saw action or interviewed those who had seen action in several wars, from Korea to Israel to Vietnam. He had ample opportunity in several environments with several armies to change his theories if they did not seem appropriate. Yet he did not do so to any great extent, as can be seen in an analysis of his writings over the period. A few specifics did change, such as his observations about how many front line soldiers took active part in combat, but by and large, his ideas remained remarkably constant.

To promote his ideas, Marshall used every resource at his disposal and acted in many capacities, from combat analyst to newspaperman. He even tried a few new roles—government consultant, publicist, and serious historian. Because these positions often overlapped, it is difficult to determine which role he was playing at any given time. Throughout the entire period, he devoted his energy to changing what he considered to need changing.

In 1950, Marshall completed another book, this time a leadership manual for all the services. This manual, *The Armed Forces Officer,* restated the ideas Marshall put forth in *Men Against Fire* and *The Soldier's Load* but also included more mundane subjects of interest to the junior officer such as the meaning of the commission, how to keep one's personal affairs in order, and the customs and courtesies of the service. Based solely on Marshall's studies, experiences, and reflections to that date, *The Armed Forces Officer* provides the historian an excellent base line from which to evaluate how subsequent experiences caused Marshall to modify his ideas. Given the opportunity to revise his manual in 1956 with the Department of the Army, and revise and republish in 1960 and again in 1975 with the Department of Defense, Marshall could have revised his explanations of how men reacted in combat. He did not.

In 1965, Brigadier General Joseph B. Sweet, senior editor of Stackpole Books, engaged Marshall to write *The Officer as a Leader* to set down the principles of leadership. Stackpole did not want "a warmed-over DOD manual."[1] While it could be based on the DOD revision of *The Armed Forces Officer,* Stackpole wanted this new version to be different in appearance and in content. But what Stackpole got was a warmed-over DOD manual. The changes made were so few and so minor that it almost looks as if Marshall dared Stackpole to change it. He added a reference here and there to Korea, Lebanon, or Vietnam, cut out a comment on this general or that one, and added three propositions to his list of how to lead Americans in combat. But the majority of the changes in the 1950 edition were made between the 1956 and 1960 editions, and even these were minor. *The Officer as a Leader* is so close to the 1960 version of *The Armed Forces Officer* as to make one wonder whether Marshall even read Sweet's letter.

An example of the degree to which this book changed—or rather, did not change—in its various forms can be found in the last chapter of each book, entitled "Americans in Combat" in all versions of *The Armed Forces Officer* and "The Leading of Americans in Combat" in *The Officer as a Leader.* This short, eight-page chapter lists about thirty premises or characteristics of American men in combat. The few changes were so inconsequential as to hardly warrant mentioning. For instance, when speaking of the American soldier, in all versions, Marshall said, "Except on a Hollywood lot, there is no such thing as an American fighter "type." Our best men come in all colors, shapes, and sizes. They appear from every section of the nation." In the original version, he had added the phrase "including the territories" to the end. That's the extent of the difference. In paragraph after paragraph, for the rest of the text, not even such small deviations as that can be found. It would seem, then, that Marshall did not find anything in the intervening years or military conflicts to change his mind about the observations and ideas he made in the 1940s. In 1969 he wrote:

> *I am well aware that the average American who has not been to Vietnam believes that the war there has nothing in common with operations against the North Koreans and Communist Chinese, against the Japanese in World War II, or the Germans in 1918. The military analyst who has worked all these fields is far more impressed by the identicalness of features, the similarity of problems, the grinding repetition of historical incident.*[2]

While the initial version of *The Armed Forces Officer* was being approved and printed in the summer of 1950, the war in Korea began. In the fall, as the Department of Defense was putting the final touches on *The Armed Forces Officer,* Marshall was approached by the Chief Historian of the Army to handle the historical work in Korea. Because of technicalities, however, his appointment fell through. But Marshall did not miss the action. The two-year-old Operations Research Office (ORO), an Army think-tank, invited him to go to Korea with several other experts as an operations analyst.[3] Marshall readily accepted.

The ORO hoped to use Korea as an opportunity to evaluate actual combat performance. Problems under study included the tactical use of atomic weapons, close air support of ground forces, employment of armor, infantry weapons systems, psychological warfare, airborne operations, and logistical support of combat. [4] Marshall signed his contract in November 1950 and was off to East Asia. [5] Arriving in Korea, Marshall was assigned to investigate the Chinese army and its tactics. [6]

After twelve days of interviewing troops and commanders as he had done in World War II, Marshall reported his findings to Lieutenant General Walton H. Walker, Eighth Army Commander. On December 16, he wrote "Notes on Chinese Company Tactics," a secret paper describing how the Chinese fought. [7] This paper was the first of several to break the myth of the Chinese as hardened, invincible killers with an almost perfect intelligence system. It threw light on four points previously misunderstood by American forces. First, most encounters that Marshall investigated in the Chongchon fight (14 of 16 engagements) were meeting engagements and not carefully planned attacks by the North Koreans. The other two were set-piece because U.S. troops had given away their positions with their campfires. Second, the bugle calls and other noise-making devices were not designed primarily for unnerving U.N. troops. They were attack signals similar to those used by the Japanese in World War II. Third, the shepherd's horn, whistle, and bugle provided various levels of command and control. Fourth, some musical instruments, like rattles, conga drums, and flutes were indeed designed to scare enemy soldiers. But the use of these musical instruments, as well as the chanting and chattering of the troops would demoralize opposing forces only so long as they were not accustomed to it. Once they were trained to what the signals meant, the men could actually take advantage of them. Four days later Marshall wrote yet another secret memorandum for the Eighth Army. In "CCF Tactics in the Envelopment of a Column" he analyzed the 2nd Infantry Division's retreat from Kunuri on November 30. [8] On January 2, 1951, he wrote "Notes on CCF Area Targets Based on CCF Tactics," in which he surmised that the enemy's success at hiding during the day was due to their cramming men into hamlets and moving at night. He suggested that B-29 strikes on likely enemy concentrations would turn their tactics into an advantage for the U.N. forces. [9] Three days later he wrote the first part of "CCF in the Attack" describing the tactics used against the 2nd Division. [10] The second part followed on January 27, chronicling the activities of the 1st Marine Division in the Koto-ri, Hagaru-ri, Yudam-ni action (popularly known as the Chosin Reservoir fight) from November 20 to December 10.

These documents were not the only results of Marshall's activities in Korea during the winter of 1950-51. He performed two other services while present in the field. First, he harangued the press about their reporting. The press reports of the performance of the Army in Korea indicated that it was smashed and broken beyond belief, that there had been mass panic, and that the soldiers had not fought well at all. Rumors were rampant about the poor showing of the 2nd Division in particular.

> *I didn't talk to the press gallery; I gave it hell. I said it had been writing irresponsible copy about a bugout army based on rumors and spook stuff from malingerers. I reminded them that the Eighth Army was in retreat, with our national affairs in crisis, and that an American wasn't divested of all moral responsibility to his nation just because he held a news job. I said: "Now I can account for the 2nd Division. I'll tell you what you need to know. If you want to argue, get up and do it now, but if you haven't got any argument to make, for God's sake quit writing stories aimed to doom your country and its cause."* [11]

Along those same lines, Marshall contributed directly to the morale of American troops. He was tasked by General Walker to improve the fighting spirit of the 2nd Division. This he did by visiting every unit he could and explaining their parts in America's efforts and generally just pepping them up much as a coach does a football team during halftime. [12]

After General Walker died in a jeep accident in December 1950, Lieutenant General Matthew B. Ridgway became the Eighth Army Commander. Soon after his arrival, Ridgway gave Marshall a special task: improve night defensive tactics, particularly the aspect of battlefield illumination. Since the U.S. Army had developed no doctrine on the subject after World War I, Marshall had to deal with it "by the seat of my pants... by-guess-and-by-God." [13] Not only did he guess at the appropriate ranges for searchlight employment, he wired Liddell Hart to tap the British military for their experience on the subject of artificial moonlight. Once again, Marshall's connections came through for him.

When he returned to the United States in April 1951, Marshall had the raw material for a lengthy report on the American infantry's performance in Korea. Originally entitled "Analysis of Infantry Operations and Weapons Usage in Korea during the Winter 1950-51," this report combined the observations and deductions of his earlier Eighth Army memoranda.[14] By August 1951, Marshall had completed his draft analysis and sent more than twenty-five copies for comment to officers who had been to Korea. The Chief of Army Field Forces issued a directive to the commandants of all Army service schools, the G-3, and G-4 concerning this now "Notes on Infantry Tactics in Korea:"

> *The memorandum contains combat lessons and source material which may be directly applied to training. Selected actions illustrate the necessity for protection of lines of communication and routes of withdrawal; the advantages to be derived from close coordination of infantry-armor task force organization; the CCF pattern of movement, use of marching fire, and emphasis on grenades; the discussion of the illuminated front is a useful adjunct to our training material; and throughout the report there is evident the lack of security measures...*[15]

A review of the final version of the report, "Commentary on Infantry Operations and Weapons Usage in Korea, Winter 1950-51," printed by the Operations Research Office on October 27, 1951, revealed that Marshall's findings fell into two categories. First, the report dealt specifically with Chinese force action and the American response. This included the Chinese use of musical instruments and the inadequacy of company-size defensive perimeters in the Korean situation. Second, the paper affirmed the points he had begun publicizing four years earlier with *Men Against Fire* and *The Soldier's Load*. Generally, Marshall's World War II observations about the behavior of men in combat were borne out by the Korean experience. For instance, "... the American soldier will never develop an adequate appreciation of what full information means to the unity of combat forces and what it requires of him until more attention is paid to that subject in the course of his training."[16] And, "In the Korean fighting, the average combat soldier, when his total load is somewhere between 38 and 45 pounds (including clothing), gets along fairly well and can march a reasonable distance, engage, and still remain relatively mobile. When the load goes above 50 pounds he becomes a drag upon the company."[17] The only major difference he noted was that whereas the percentage of firers in World War II seldom rose above 15-25 percent, in Korea "when the ground and situation permit it, the measure of willing participation is more than double World War II averages. **In nighttime perimeter defense, the majority of those present actually take a personal part in the return of fire**. The chronic non-firer is an exception under the conditions of the Korean fighting."[18] Marshall attributed the increase not only to better training in the interwar years and to the peculiar nature of the Korean terrain, but also to improved low-level communications.

Although the war in Korea had stabilized, it was far from over. The attention of the military remained riveted on the front. As part of this absorption with military action, Marshall's ORO reports were in high demand. On 16 February 1953, Major General C.D. Eddleman, Assistant Chief of Staff, G-3, wrote to the Chief of Army Field Forces that the present supply of Marshall's "Commentary" had been exhausted and would not be reprinted unless the field commands indicated that a large supply was required. At that point the Fifth Army submitted a request for 668 more copies.[19]

When Marshall returned to the United States in April 1951 to resume his role as journalist, he drew on his most recent experiences to convince the American public that the soldiers in Korea were not the cowards they had been painted as being.[20] He felt driven to set the record straight, for he truly believed in the American fighting man and was deeply disappointed with the press. Articles and books published after this time evidence his deep pride in the American military.

In 1953, Marshall returned to Korea, this time as a correspondent. By pure luck, he was visiting a friend, Major General Arthur Trudeau, commander of the 7th Infantry Division, when the first Battle of Pork Chop Hill occurred. He was the only correspondent to participate as the others were at Panmunjom covering the first prisoner exchange.[21] He conducted his after-action group interviews, and his battlefield notes served as the basis for a later book

by the same name.[22] It was during this trip that the Director of the Neurop-
sychiatric Division of the Army Medical Service Graduate School at the Walter Reed Army Medical Center was moved to write to his superiors that
Marshall's method provided a useful tool not only for gathering tactical information, but also for gaining insight into the psychological processes of men under extreme stress.[23]

In the 1950s it became obvious that Marshall's observations and techniques had impacted beyond the American military. The Israelis had also "discovered" him. When the second Arab-Israeli war broke out in 1956, Marshall
was invited into Israel despite a ban by the American government. The key
elements in his success were the intervention of Colonel Katriel Salmon, the
Israeli military attache, and the fact that the Israelis had pirated both *The
Soldier's Load* (printed in Hebrew in 1952) and *Men Against Fire* (published
in Hebrew in 1956). Marshall's ideas had so impressed the Israelis that they
smuggled him into the country. Marshall was one of only two correspondents
allowed into the Sinai. In addition, the Zahal (Israeli Defense Force) not only
allowed him to interview their troops, but urged him to teach their own men
how to do it.[24] Out of his interviews and a return trip there the next year, Marshall wrote *Sinai Victory* which described the war and analyzed the Israeli's
application of doctrine.

Obviously impressed with the Israeli army and no doubt feeling a warm
glow of satisfaction that **someone** had been listening to him, Marshall now
had proof of the validity of his arguments.

> *On returning to the United States, I told the leaders of our
> General Staff once again that we should pay heed to the Israeli
> Army. It had much to teach us, more probably than we could give
> it. I ticked off the [techniques] and policies that we should
> examine—night firing, snap shooting, the use of Class 4 and 5
> material (low IQs) within the military, and the field training of field
> officers in combat decision-making. The suggestions fell on deaf
> ears.[25]*

Renewed interest in Marshall's interview technique emerged in the early
stages of the Vietnam conflict, however. In 1964 and again in 1966, the
military asked for his assistance in clearing the fog of battle. The 1964 trip
was cancelled, possibly because Secretary of Defense McNamara found

Marshall's recent column in the *Detroit News* so critical of him that he could not abide seeing Marshall get any sort of help or encouragement from the government.[26] On his two trips to Vietnam in 1966, Marshall trained several officers in the after-action interview technique and collected enough interview notes to write six books on Vietnam.[27] At about the same time, several articles appeared in professional military journals describing the interview technique and urging its adoption by the entire Army.[28]

Although the Army adopted his interview technique only slowly and fitfully in the era of the Arab-Israeli and Vietnam wars, it did make use of his basic ideas on the effectiveness of its soldiers. In January 1954, the Operations Research Office published a report which substantiated many of Marshall's claims about men in battle. "Human Factors in Military Operations" contained three chapters that bore directly on subjects which Marshall had investigated—fatigue, fear, and panic. The chairman of the Department of Psychology at the University of Maryland, drawing solely on scientific research, concluded that there was indeed a relationship between fatigue and fear.[29] Examining the phenomenon of fear, Dr. Neal A. Miller supported Marshall's assertions that of the many causes of fear, lack of knowledge of the situation, fatigue, and fear of killing another human being were among the most important.[30] Studies of this sort continued for several years. The Human Resources Research Office (HumRRO), ORO's counterpart at George Washington University, published four studies dealing with training and leadership, drawing heavily on the Korean War. Those studies validated many of Marshall's ideas.[31] One, "Trainfire I," tested exactly the kind of marksmanship training that Marshall had recommended years before, replacing the known-distance range with a combat course. This system was adopted by the Army in 1958.[32]

In July 1957, HumRRO published "Trainfire II," the platoon-level sequel to its marksmanship program. Six months later, HumRRO finished a study regarding the pre-selection of suitable soldiers, "Fighter I: An Analysis of Combat Fighters and Non-Fighters."[33] The report began with the premises Marshall had brought forward in *Men Against Fire* and noted the need to implement a long-range effort to increase the number of good performers in infantry combat units.[34]

The Army also addressed the problem of overloading the soldier. The Quartermaster Research and Development Command conducted research into this area and sent Marshall copies of their findings along with the promise that they would send more as they became available. According to the introduction to their report, progress was made in the subject largely through Marshall's making the problem public.[35] The Army also began research into the psychological aspects of combat and considered Marshall an expert on the subject. In April 1954, he spoke before a Graduate Symposium of the Medical Service Graduate School at Walter Reed. The subject of his talk was combat stress. According to the letter of invitation from the school's commandant, the notes of all speakers were to be printed to "constitute a textbook of the most recent and pertinent professional lessons in military medicine. These volumes will fulfill a definite need in the educational programs of the Armed Forces, Civilian Defense, and American medical colleges..."[36]

The next year, 1955, Marshall was appointed to a panel investigating the conduct of American POWs in the Korean War. This was not the first contact Marshall had with prisoners of war, for in World War II, before joining the Historical Branch, he had been involved with the relocation of America's POWs, the Japanese Americans.[37] Later, while at Kwajalein, he was given the extra duty of determining how to soften Japanese resistance and get them to surrender.[38] In Korea, General Mark Clark, General Ridgway's successor as UN Commander, had sent for Marshall to help with the first exchange of prisoners.[39] With this background, Marshall became a consultant to the Office of the Assistant Secretary of Defense for Research and Development. The Secretary had charged this panel with the investigation of psychological warfare, Special Forces operations, and escape and evasion training in the Armed Forces. Marshall served on the committee for escape and evasion, and so became involved in the drafting of the Code of Conduct. This policy, which later became effective as one of President Eisenhower's executive orders, was intended to prescribe the actions expected of captured American military personnel. Marshall, the primary author of the Code, tried to keep it simple and practical. The main thrust of the Code was to permit the prisoner to engage in a game of wits with the enemy and not to limit his response to his name, rank, and serial number.[40]

This work was Marshall's introduction to Vietnam. In 1962 he appeared before the Advisory Committee on Non-Military Instruction chaired by the Undersecretary of the Army Karl L. Benedetson. Concerned about operations already begun in Vietnam, the Secretary of Defense commissioned this investigation to see how well the military was preparing its troops for possible capture and internment. In other words, were the men sufficiently indoctrinated in the Code of Conduct to enable them to withstand torture and imprisonment? One of several witnesses, Marshall spoke about command responsibility. Benedetson and Allen Dulles were so impressed with his statement that they invited Marshall to accompany them on a whirlwind tour of the Pacific and Far East, to include Vietnam, to gauge the state of training in the theater. In a month's time, they flew from Oahu to Midway, Hong Kong, Manila, and Saigon. Their follow-up report, published in July, indicated that Code of Conduct training was being neglected.[41] This trip was the first of four Marshall was to make to Southeast Asia.

Besides the committees on prisoners of war and the Code of Conduct, Marshall served on many other advisory boards and commissions, ranging from investigations of the possible uses of such drugs as LSD, to the provision of foreign aid.[42] Yet he sensed he was not having the success he had in the immediate post-World War II period. Although government agencies called on him frequently, and for a variety of reasons, he characterized the period after his Korean adventures as "that decade when I was wallowing in the bureaucracy."[43]

But Marshall had not forsaken his role as master storyteller. With the publication of *The River and the Gauntlet* in 1954, he continued the sort of history that he had begun with *Island Victory*. His narrative histories combined his skills as storyteller, combat historian, and operations analyst. Before he died he wrote twelve such books, each taken almost exclusively from his field notes as historian/analyst.[44] For instance, *Night Drop* and *Battle at Best* are drawn from his World War II field notes and complement *Men Against Fire* and *The Soldier's Load*. Likewise, *The River and the Gauntlet* comes from the notes of his 1950-51 interviews with the troops that had been hit by the Chinese on the Chongchon River.[45]

These books, written in a popular, easy-to-read style, attracted many readers both within the military and without. Some scholars have decided

Marshall's books are less than "good history." Preferring copious documentation and less drama, these historians have been a major stumbling block to the new oral history, which is just now gaining a foothold in the academic community. But scholarship aside, because of his style and the dramatic sequence of events portrayed in his books, many soldiers—and not just officers—came to read Marshall's narratives. And in them, they were exposed not only to history but also to Marshall's theory of what makes a good soldier. In other words, by couching his theory in books that appealed to a wide spectrum of readers, Marshall reached more people than he would have if he had been a purely scholarly writer, writing carefully footnoted and researched works and publishing in less quantity.

Next to his writings, one of his most influential services to the U.S. Army involved lecturing to service schools. Since the late 1940s he had been a frequent speaker at every level of military school from the National War College down to the branch schools at Fort Knox, Fort Benning, Fort Sill and others. The subjects on which he spoke varied, but most often related to the human element in combat. He not only spoke at American military posts but also in foreign countries. At the British Staff College at Camberley in 1964, John Keegan, eminent military historian and senior lecturer of military history at the Royal Military Academy at Sandhurst, met Marshall for the first time. His impression was very revealing:

> *[Marshall] exuded energy and vulgarity in about equal measure. But I did infallibly detect that he was someone apart and above any military historian I had met before. I subsequently came to believe, as I still do, that he was touched by genius.*[46]

Response to Marshall and his ideas had always been mixed. Even (or perhaps especially) *Men Against Fire* had not received universal acclaim. Many misunderstood Marshall to be saying that the American soldier was a coward. Some felt personally affronted by Marshall's writings, inevitably focusing almost exclusively on the controversial "25 percent rule." Nothing could have been further from the truth. Marshall believed in heroes and repeatedly asserted that America had its fair share of them.

1. Letter from Joseph B. Sweet, July 23, 1965, found in the MC.

2. S.L.A. Marshall, *Ambush* (New York: Cowles Book Company, Inc., 1969), pp. 3-4.

3. Marshall, *Bringing Up the Rear*, p. 179.

4. Edward M. Parker, "Trial by Combat," *Combat Forces Journal* (May 1951): 16. This description of ORO is further elaborated in Herbert Yahraes, "The Mysterious Mission of ORO," *Saturday Evening Post* (February 23, 1952).

5. Travel orders found in the MC.

6. Marshall, *Bringing Up the Rear*, p. 180.

7. "Notes on Chinese Company Tactics," ORO-S-41 (EUSAK), (SECRET), by S.L.A. Marshall, dated December 16, 1950. Copy 19 of 25 is in the MC. The paper Marshall wrote after the meeting was probably HQ, EUSAK, Combat Information Bulletin #6, dated December 17, 1950, signed by Lieutenant General Walker, and also entitled "Notes on Chinese Company Tactics." Both are found in the MC.

8. "CCF Tactics in the Envelopment of a Column," Staff Memorandum ORO-S-25 (EUSAK), (SECRET), by S.L.A. Marshall, dated December 20, 1950. Copy 48 of 50 is in the MC.

9. "Notes on CCF Area Targets Based on CCF Tactics," ORO-S-4 (SECRET), by S.L.A. Marshall, dated January 2, 1951. Copy 49 of 50 is in the MC.

10. "CCF in the Attack," Part I, ORO-S-26 (EUSAK), dated January 5, 1951; and Part II, ORO-S-34 (EUSAK), dated January 27, 1951. Copy 15 of 50 of Part I and 92 of 150 of Part II are in the MC.

11. Marshall, *Bringing Up the Rear*, pp. 182-3.

12. Ibid., pp. 188-9.

13. Ibid., p. 190.

14. Response to the author's questionnaire, dated August 12, 1983.

15. Directive from Office, Chief of Army Field Forces, ATTNG-64 300.6/14(C), December 11, 1951.

16. "Commentary on Infantry Operations and Weapons Usage in Korea, Winter of 1950-51," ORO-R-13 (RESTRICTED), by S.L.A. Marshall, October 27, 1951, p. 27.

17. Ibid., p. 47.

18. Ibid. pp. 4-5.

19. Second Endorsement, G-3 040 (January 24, 1953), Subject: ORO-R-13, "Commentary on Infantry Operations and Weapons Usage in Korea," from OACofS, G-3, Dept of the Army, Washington, D.C., February 16, 1953, to Chief, Army Field Forces, Fort Monroe, Virginia, found in the MC.

20. Years later, during the Vietnam War, the Army asked him—unofficially—to perform the role of pro-Army publicist again. Specifically, the Chief of the Center of Military History asked Marshall to write a narrative for popular consumption, showing the fine job that the troops in Vietnam were doing. See the letter from Brigadier General Hal C. Pattison, March 31, 1966, in the MC.

21. Marshall had a part in the initial steps of the exchange, a fact which would contribute to his service later as an expert in prisoner of war investigations.

22. Marshall, *Bringing Up the Rear,* pp. 218-9. General Trudeau corroborated this account in an interview with the author on August 18, 1983. He said that Marshall lived with him in his field headquarters, during which time they spent many hours discussing tactics, organization and equipment. Further, he said Marshall met the patrol when they returned—though he gave the time as 0500 hours. This account is what was referred to in the first chapter regarding the short time period between an engagement and Marshall's interview of the participants.

23. Ibid., p. 220. Also, David McK. Rioch, M.D., "Report on Temporary Duty in Japan and Korea, 14 April to 17 July 1953," unpublished report, pp. 31-2, found in the MC.

24. Marshall, *Bringing Up the Rear,* pp. 235ff. That Marshall was urged to teach the Israelis how to conduct interviews has been verified by Colonel Shobtai Noi, Ph.D., Head of the Mental Health Research Division, Mental Health Department of the IDF Medical Corps, in an interview with the author on August 15, 1983. He said that the techniques now used in the IDF are directly traceable to Marshall.

25. Marshall, *Bringing Up the Rear,* p. 245.

26. Ibid., pp. 269-70. Corroborating documents, including a letter of apology from K.M. Sullivan, administrative officer at the Institute for Defense Analysis, May 19, 1964, found in the MC.

27. The first time the United States government showed interest, 1964, the Institute for Defense Analysis, which provided advice to the Defense Department's Directorate of Research and Engineering, wrote, "We have come to understand that there is an inadequate understanding of the military problems and hence of the R&D requirements in these remote areas, particularly in Vietnam. A possible means of clarifying the situation is combat interviews of the kind you successfully conducted in Korea, the Sinai campaign, and World War II." See the letter from Joseph Coates to Marshall, December 18, 1963, in the MC.

28. Lieutenant Colonel Frank L. Brown, "Pass on that Combat Lore," Army (September 1966): 66ff. This article included an abridged section of chapter one of *Island Victory.* See also Lieutenant Colonel David Hackworth, "Battle Analysis, *Army* (July 1967): 33-7.

29. Thomas G. Andrews, "Human Factors in Military Operations," ORO-T-259, Richard Hays Williams, ed., p. 253.

30. Neal A. Miller, "Human Factors in Military Operations," ORO-T-259, Richard Hays Williams, ed., p. 274.

31. "Tactical Training of the Infantry Rifle Squad," GWU HRRO TR-18, M. Dean Havron, et al., June 1955; "Development of Proficiency Tests for Basic Combat and Light Infantry Training," GWU HRRO T-19, Robert A. Baker, et al., July 1955; "Leadership in Rifle Squads on the Korean Front Line," GWU HRRO TR-21, Rodney A. Clark, September 1955; "Trainfire I: A New Course in Basic Rifle Marksmanship," Howard H. McFann, et al., October 1955.

32. In a letter to a researcher, Mr. Bruce G. Wilkins, dated September 26, 1978, John J. Slonaker, Chief of the Historical Reference Section of the Military History Institute wrote, "Apparently, Marshall's warning did not result in any timely or effective remedy, because the Korean War produced widespread concern, plus a number of studies, on the high percentage of non-firers and poor marksmen in combat. Recognition of the problem led to research and development by the US Army Infantry Human Research Unit for a fresh approach to teaching basic rifle

marksmanship. The result was the Trainfire courses of instruction, implemented during fiscal year 1958." Copy of the letter in the author's possession.

33. "Trainfire II: A New Course in Basic Technique of Fire and Squad Tactics," GWU HRRO TR-41, John A. Hammes, et al., July 1957.

34. "Fighters: An Analysis of Combat Fighters and Non-Fighters," GWU HRRO TR-44, Robert L. Egbert, et al., December 1957, p. 3.

35. Letter from William F. Pounder, acting Chief, Research Services Office, Headquarters, Quartermaster Research and Development Command, dated November 18, 1955, and the report enclosed, MC. The Navy, on behalf of the Marines, also came to Marshall for help concerning the soldier's load. Investigating the problems of providing practical "armored garments," such as the flak jacket, Marshall was asked to contribute his ideas on the advantages and costs of such equipment. They had identified the problem of overloading as one of the major costs, and hence came to Marshall—not once but twice, in 1957 and 1967. See the letter from Commander F.J. Lewis, USN, Head, Department of Personnel Protection, U.S. Naval Medical Field Research Laboratory, dated February 14, 1957, found in the MC; letter from Captain Jesse F. Adams, USN, Commander, Naval Field Research Laboratory, July 27, 1967, MC.

36. Letter from Colonel William S. Stone, Commandant, Army Medical Service Graduate School, dated January 4, 1954, found in the MC. This school later became the Walter Reed Army Institute of Research.

37. Marshall, *Bringing Up the Rear,* pp. 53.

38. Ibid., p. 74.

39. Ibid., p. 215.

40. Marshall's description of his part in the project can be found in *Bringing Up the Rear,* pp. 225ff and 259ff. Marshall continued his involvement with the Code when in 1976 he served on the Defense Review Committee for the Code of Conduct.

41. Ibid., p. 260.

42. His work on the field manual's early draft is shown by a letter from General W. E. DePuy, Commanding General of the United States Training and Doctrine Command, July 15, 1976, in which the General thanked Marshall for his help and enclosed a copy of the new manual. Letter found in the MC.

43. Marshall, *Bringing Up the Rear,* p. 229.

44. *Island Victory* (1945), *Bastogne* (1946), *The River and the Gauntlet* (1953), *Pork Chop Hill* (1956), *Sinai Victory* (1958), *Night Drop* (1962), *Battle at Best* (1963), *Battles in the Monsoon (1967), Bird (1968), West to Cambodia* (1968), *Ambush* (1969), and *Vietnam—Three Battles* (1971).

45. According to Robert Leckie, author of *March to Glory,* the story of the Marines' fight from encirclement at the Chosin reservoir, Marshall provided notes of his interviews with the Marines to Leckie. "Much of the book's validity—especially of the Marines of the Fifth and Seventh Regiments coming down the road from the reservoir—is due to [Marshall's] notes." See the letter from Robert Leckie to the author, August 17, 1983.

46. John Keegan, "Battle and the Historian," *International Security* (Winter 1978-79): 145.

CHAPTER FIVE

THE QUESTION OF INFLUENCE

M *arshall' s] ultimate purpose in writing was not merely to describe and analyze... but to persuade the American Army that it was fighting its wars the wrong way... His arguments were consonantly effective, so that he had the unusual experience for a historian of seeing his message not merely accepted in his own lifetime but translated into practice.*

John Keegan

For decades S.L.A. Marshall has been widely and frequently quoted, yet his actual influence and impact are difficult to distill. Marshall's influence actually consisted of two separate elements: his immediate impact on the Army as an institution, and the way he influenced soldiers individually. Marshall acted as the Army's catalyzing force in the years following World War II. He devoted over thirty years to the improvement of a system to which he was deeply committed, all the while believing that he was having no impact. His ideas seemed to catch on and then fade away. But in fact, Marshall's observations and suggestions led to many improvements.

Marshall himself constantly noted that his "truths" were pure common sense—perhaps not immediately evident, but certainly readily acceptable and easily grasped. But institutions and institutional thinking are hard to change. Most of Marshall's proposed reforms, sound though they were, met stiff resistance at worst and inertia at best. Fortunately his background and experience prepared him well for what he considered his struggle to improve the fighting forces of the United States.

Marshall's early career as a newspaperman readied him for the jobs that lay ahead. The variety of his assignments and their fast-paced nature required adaptability and a flexible personality. His undying interest for things military and his humanitarian concern for the common man readily merged with the drive and passion that continually impelled Marshall into the field. As a young writer he honed the style that was to bring him a wide audience when he set about composing narrative histories later in his career.

Marshall's work as a military analyst, however, did not begin until World War II. During the early war years he had made a name for himself in the Detroit area, not only as a newspaperman, but as a radio commentator. His outspoken manner and unsettling ideas very often stirred up controversy. Paying close attention to the events unfolding in Europe in 1939, he predicted German intention and strategy. Those ideas he worked into a book he called *Blitzkrieg.* While it was still in manuscript form, the events he foresaw took place. In 1941, Marshall wrote another book, *Armies on Wheels,* which predicted that the German invasion of Russia would fail. His predictions were derived from observation and a mind trained to military thought and analysis by extensive reading of the two most progressive military theorists and historians of the interwar era, J.F.C. Fuller and B.H. Liddell Hart.

As a combat historian in the newly created Historical Branch from 1943 until he left active duty in May 1946, Marshall contributed several innovations to the way the United States Army approached military history. His discovery of the group afteraction interview technique added significantly to the body of combat knowledge and dispelled the fog of war, as documents alone could not do. Adopted by some combat historians, this method not only supplied important data for the multi-volumed history, *The United States Army in World War II,* it also provided commanders with valuable and timely information on friendly and enemy tactics.

As Deputy and then Chief of the Historical Section, European Theater of Operations, Marshall helped get that organization producing at maximum capacity and managed to keep enough historians together in the face of rapid demobilization to prepare the records they had amassed during the war. An outgrowth of this activity were the interviews with senior German officers—an accomplishment that produced information on how the Soviets had operated on the Eastern Front and provided post-war tacticians with valuable intelligence insight.

Following his return to civilian life in 1946, Marshall wrote several articles, later to become books, which drew together his observations on the war and presented explanations of why some soldiers fight better than others. Marshall's most startling revelation came out of his combat observations in both the Pacific and European theaters and rocked the military community. Based on what he witnessed and investigated, less than 25 percent of infantry riflemen fired their weapons in combat, even when directly engaged. In his first analytical book, *Men Against Fire,* Marshall brought this statistic forward and concentrated on what he considered to be obvious reasons for this tactical deficiency. Marshall stressed that all training should concentrate on improving the active participation of soldiers in combat. According to his observations in World War II, only a small proportion of the men on the front line actually fired at the enemy, and it seemed that it was always the same men who carried the unit forward. To increase participation, Marshall urged that the Army improve unit cohesion—the bonding of each soldier with his comrades. To do this, he emphasized person-to-person communication. Without that link, men confronted with danger felt isolated and shrank back in fear. Therefore, small unit leaders had to be attuned to ways of enhancing communication. In so saying, Marshall stressed the importance of what Napoleon called the moral over the physical.

Marshall had pinpointed poor communication as the main factor behind the fear he saw manifested on the battlefield. To this he added several contributing influences. To counter the recruit's unrealistic expectations of combat, Marshall urged realistic training—letting soldiers know that combat consisted not of constant activity but long periods of boredom punctuated by moments of intense excitement. He urged the system to train the soldier to expect the feelings of isolation and fear and not to be overwhelmed by them. One means of improving training, Marshall postulated, was to conduct a more realistic combat marksmanship course, on which trainees fired at pop-up silhouettes and nonhuman targets under simulated combat conditions. An important element in training was directed at small unit leaders. According to Marshall, they needed to know not merely how to improve the soldier's performance, but as leaders, they needed more: training in anticipating and improvising so they could react to the vicissitudes of combat; practice in giving clear, forceful orders of the sort which motivates men in the face of danger and indecision; and education in determining what information might be useful to other commanders. In *Men Against Fire,* Marshall painted a vivid picture of the human dynamics of combat.

Following close on the heels of *Men Against Fire* came *The Soldier's Load and the Mobility of a Nation,* Marshall's second major contribution to military thought. In this book, he drew on his wartime experiences and interviews and suggested that fear and fatigue had a relationship which few people were aware of but which had enormous implications in combat. Simply stated, a tired soldier frightens easily and a frightened soldier tires rapidly. His theory led to investigations which are still being conducted. But, more important, the theory led to a general concern for keeping the soldier's load within a limit that would not detract from his combat performance. Taken together, the two books contained a highly developed and innovative system for understanding men in combat. From 1950 until his death in 1977, Marshall did not significantly modify his ideas. He found them applicable in the Korean, Arab-Israeli, and Vietnam wars.

Marshall was a pioneer in the two major fields in which he worked—military history and military theory. He presented a new approach for obtaining the sequence of events in combat, an inherently chaotic situation. As a by-product of his investigation of small unit actions, he developed the then novel theory of human behavior under stress, articulating the relationship between fear, fatigue, communication, training, and leadership in a way never done before. In two relatively short, easily readable books, he brought to light insights and connections that others had seen only dimly.

Marshall wrote his books with an eye to changing the U.S. Army. He had noted deficiencies in the force and used the forum of his books to propose reforms. His aim was not to lay blame but to improve. Marshall worked against the strong forces of institutional resistance to change and a zealous new faith in technology and systems analysis. Moreover, the Army was in a constant state of flux from both internal and external causes—from the

80

constant turnover of personnel, and from the larger environment in which it operated. In addition, Marshall's ideas, though surprisingly simple when taken one by one, form a web whose complexities are difficult to assimilate, much less act upon directly. Marshall's personality and audience also affected the way he was received. All of these factors must be examined before presenting a full conclusion about the nature and degree of his influence on the military.

By its very nature, the Army is not an organization easily reformed. Not only its size but also the frequency with which leaders change positions make lasting reform difficult. Even when chiefs of staff attempt to make changes, they encounter both active and passive resistance in the form of ingrained habits, misunderstandings, and personal preferences, not to mention power politics and basic bureaucratic inertia.

Another internal influence involves the policy of rotating soldiers. The effects of frequent personnel transfers on small units are well documented. But the effects are even more exaggerated at the level of high command. A program which receives the full backing of one commander may die of neglect when another commander with a new set of priorities and personal preferences takes over. Sometimes the old programs are retained but not given the attention they once received merely because the new commander wants to make a name for himself as an innovator in his own right. The same holds true for staff officers. All seek not only to do their best for the organization, but also to improve their careers. Out of such realities come lost causes as well as important new ideas. What this constant change meant to men on the outside, like Marshall, was that the struggle was neverending. Every year or two there were new people to convince and new policies to fight.

Besides the flux caused by personnel transfers and changes in doctrine, additional internal resistance is generated by factional infighting. When one branch, or for that matter major service, vies with another for the limited resources of the defense establishment, ideas and policies may be lost in the shuffle. Ideas which show great potential may be discarded as having too great a price, either financial or political. Just as compromises are made in the legislative branches of government, so too are they made in the military.

In addition to the internal inhibitors, Marshall's ideas had to contend with several external factors. The American political system tends to work against lasting changes in the armed forces. When a new president enters office, he may bring with him men of a different outlook, whose decisions are based on thought processes and assumptions that stand apart from those of the previous administration. Policy and doctrine set at this level may change as often as every four years.

Another, more subtle, external influence which worked against Marshall's ideas was postwar society's growing faith in technology. If there was a single theme that ran through Marshall's efforts from 1946 to his death in 1977, it was that the machine could never replace the fighting man. Yet it would be wrong to infer that the phenomenon of blind faith in technology was a product solely of the postwar world. The impact of science and technology on military theory began long before Marshall tried to change the Army. Accompanying the changes in tactical doctrine from 1946 through 1976 was the conviction that the nation's technical superiority would provide for the national security. The military journals of the period overflow with articles advertising the latest and best new weapon in the inventory or on the drawing board. An unfortunate result of the overemphasis on technology was a loss of concern for training the individual soldier. Marshall attempted to counteract the prevailing faith in technology, a difficult task on top of the other obstacles he faced.

The advent of systems analysis was a further counterforce to Marshall's focus on the soldier. In the 1960s, the new Secretary of Defense for the Kennedy administration, Robert S. McNamara, introduced to the military the systems analysis approach to problem solving. Introducing civilian management techniques, the so-called "number crunchers" took the military by storm. The controversy over the applicability of these techniques to military organization has not yet subsided. Simply put, the question was: is the officer primarily a manager or a leader? Marshall ran afoul of McNamara largely because of their divergent views on this issue. Marshall's emphasis on the intangibles of combat had no place in the quantification process espoused by the Defense Secretary. With the forces of officialdom behind him, McNamara reoriented an entire generation of officers to the systems analysis way of thinking. Marshall, who could count only on his friends and his own writing, had a hard time keeping the idea alive that security in general and mobility and leadership in particular were not quantifiable entities derived from masses of weapons, vehicles, or systems. Human nature also counted.

Yet another factor inhibiting acceptance of Marshall's ideas was the missing framework for those ideas, a framework which he sought to erect. Marshall's ideas about leadership, motivation, morale, communication, fear, and fatigue, when taken separately, were hardly unfamiliar in military circles. What he did was to articulate their complex interrelationship. By articulating the relationship, Marshall rejuvenated some old ideas while he stimulated thinking in professional soldiers the world over. Regardless of the truth of his ideas or of the validity of his group interview method, he set a standard to which subsequent generations of historians and soldiers were compelled to refer, even when they chose to reject the standard.[1]

While Marshall's ideas, taken separately, were neither new nor difficult, they were hard to understand as an integrated whole because Marshall's theory dealt with the vague factors of fear, fatigue, and group psychology, as well as with historical accuracy. In a field so new that the vocabulary had not yet been agreed upon, it was difficult to present new ideas, much less to gain their widespread acceptance.

Marshall's introduction of the group interview method pointed up the problem of historical accuracy in the reconstruction of a battle, while introducing a new means to that end. Basing his theory on personal observation of combat and on his own interviews, Marshall left his conclusions open to criticism. When he argued that the training methods of the 1930s and 1940s did not prepare men adequately for combat, he sparked a controversy that polarized U.S. Army officers. Those who did not agree questioned the argument's validity by calling Marshall's credentials into question. To them, he was a self-serving journalist, not a professional officer; a pedantic critic, not a commander; an outsider, not a combat soldier. The implication was that the categories were mutually exclusive. That is, a journalist could not provide insight which professional officers lacked; a critic could not offer valuable information for commanders; an outside observer could not be accurate in his reporting.

The arguments against Marshall tended to cloud the issue. The accuracy of an observation or a conclusion does not rest solely on the observer's background. Other, more objective criteria must be applied, such as the observations of others in similar battle situations. Many critics affirmed the validity of Marshall's observations and conclusions. Yet many disagreed—even acerbically. The violence of the disagreement, however, should not sway the mind of an objective student of the issue. Some critics, in their attack, for example, on Marshall's 25 percent firing ratio, betrayed a vested interest in its invalidity, seeing the ratio as a reflection of their own combat leadership.

Aside from vested interests, there were other explanations for the controversy over Marshall's 25 percent firing ratio. Some World War II combat leaders who claimed that all their men fought consistently not only saw what they wanted to see, but also suffered from the kind of blindness that combat causes. Under fire, the soldier's span of vision is shortened, not only literally by terrain, obstacles, and vegetation, but pyschologically by his concern for survival. Also, leaders may assume that the men in their immediate vicinity are representative of all the men under their command. When one of Marshall's critics maintained that even during the chaotic circumstances of an airborne assault he witnessed all his men acting aggressively, he may have overlooked two factors. First, his presence would be likely to motivate those around him to fight aggressively. Second, if one of his men were hiding and refusing to take part, is it likely that he would be noticed by a leader intent on getting on with the mission?

Not all Marshall's critics were World War II veterans. Some who served in the Korean and Vietnamese conflicts have found it hard to believe that only 25 percent of line troops fired their weapons. In their experience, nearly all troops took part in firefights. For them, the discrepancy between their own experience and Marshall's statistic calls all of Marshall's ideas into question. A study of Marshall's views on the issue, however, reveals that he observed an increase in participation in firefights from one war to the next. The observations of *Men Against Fire* were not the only ones that Marshall made. This misinterpretation—that he intended the 25 percent firing ratio to be a timeless universal verity—would naturally call all his ideas into question. That is why it is important to note that the 25 percent firing ratio was an historical observation, made of a particular group of people (infantry riflemen) of a particular culture (20th century America) at a particular time (1943-1945). It was a snapshot, not a moving picture.

For his part, Marshall thought he had made only two major contributions to military thought: his technique for lifting the fog of battle, and the reciprocal relationship between fear and fatigue.[2] He had, however, done much more. In publicizing his ideas forcefully and persistently over three decades, Marshall focused the attention of both the military and the public on matters which deserved attention. His observations concerning the strength of cohesive units and the problems of communication on the tactical and interpersonal level have generated many studies on those subjects. Likewise, his most controversial and most misunderstood observations about active participation in combat led research organizations to investigate new methods of marksmanship training. Finally, in the field of military history, his technique provided a proven, effective method of complementing documentary research.[3]

While not all of Marshall's innovations have influenced the Army of the late twentieth century, some of them continue to make themselves felt. In the late 1980s, the Army trained its soldiers in a marksmanship program similar to Trainfire.[4] The logical derivative of that program is in use in tank gunnery training, including firing on the move at pop-up silhouettes under simulated combat conditions over varied terrain. Scientists at the Walter Reed Army Institute of Research rest their current studies of fear and fatigue on Marshall's writings.[5] In the January 1987 issue of *Military Review,* a psychologist at Walter Reed co-authored an article entitled "Soldier Overloading in Grenada," based heavily on both *Men Against Fire* and *The Soldier's Load.* Built upon Marshall's observations and analysis, the article also included interviews with participants. In the 1980s, the Command and General Staff College included *Men Against Fire* on its mandatory reading list. Certainly the most visible publication which drew on Marshall's insights was the 1983 edition of FM 22-100, *Military Leadership.* The manual incorporated and elucidated his observations on cohesion, fatigue, fear, isolation, and information.

In his attempt to reform the Army, Marshall used every means at his disposal—from his writing to his personal contacts. He influenced and impressed a wide range of soldiers, from squad leader to general. He contributed directly to the Army's tactical effectiveness in Korea through papers written under the auspices of the Operations Research Office. In those papers, as in much of his writing, the focus was on combat performance, training, and the fear-fatigue relationship. His group interview technique received attention not only in Korea but also in Israel and Vietnam, and because no government agency had institutionalized it, Marshall was repeatedly asked to train men in the method. This anomaly—the Army's periodic and repeated resort to an historical technique it never institutionalized—was a good example of the forgetfulness that plagued Marshall's relationship with the Army. The same pattern was evident in Marshall's insights about the fatigue-fear relationship, marksmanship training, and unit cohesion. All in all, while doctrine was developed and implemented to address those areas, by Marshall's standards, progress was painfully slow. While he enjoyed great influence in high places, in retrospect it was probably his influence on the junior officers of the immediate post-World War II and Korean War era which bore the most fruit. Many of those men, having read Marshall's analytical and narrative books, and having heard him speak at one or another of the service schools, carried his insights directly into combat.

That Marshall had a direct impact on Army training, based on his observations in Korea and after, cannot be denied, though he was not a trainer in his own right. More definitely he was a an analyst, a military thinker. Not a "licensed" historian, he was certainly a reporter of historical events. As a writer and thinker on many military subjects, he enlisted his considerable communications skills to excite readers' passions. Indeed, he had a genius for arousing both soldiers and civilians to action. His ideas affected many military issues, but none so significantly as those relating to combat at the small unit level. In this area alone—had he contributed nothing else—Marshall could claim to be one of the most influential men of his century. Marshall himself wrote, "A military critic is not an innovator but a catalyst who brings to focus the thoughts of his associates."[6] That comment may indeed best sum up his particular gift.

During the Vietnam conflict, the Defense Department convinced Marshall to teach his method to a new crop of historians.[7] The attempt was made to continue the sort of lessons learned approach he had developed earlier. Elements of the technique have survived in various forms in the post-Vietnam period. A prime example is the crucial learning in field exercises that occurs during the after-action portion of the program known as Realtrain, a training system designed for small units in the early 1970s and modeled after Marshall's post-battle interview sessions.[8] In its training programs, Realtrain further advanced Marshall's proposals.[9] Created to simulate battlefield conditions and provide a realistic training environment, Realtrain addressed one of Marshall's primary concerns—that training bore no resemblance to combat. It was instituted as the Vietnam conflict was drawing to a close amid sharp criticism that training deficiencies had hindered the United States' ability to fight and win. Further examination of the American military performance in Vietnam led to the establishment of the Center for Army Lessons Learned in August 1985. This body was created to collect observations from United States and foreign combat operations and exercises and distill from them lessons applicable in future conflicts. Marshall's exhortations, while not incorporated into Army doctrine of the 1950s or 1960s, as he may have liked, are today being implemented.

Perhaps the most important single set of programs based on Marshall's ideas were those that General Edward C. Meyer instituted during his term as Chief of Staff of the Army between 1979 and 1983: the COHORT and regimental systems. General Meyer placed great emphasis on educating Army leaders on the purposes behind these innovations.[10] Developed in 1981 as a part of the Army's New Manning System, his policies were designed to keep soldiers and leaders together longer to foster unit affiliation and loyalty. The primary aim was to enable soldiers to better withstand the initial shock of battle. The implementation of the COHORT and regimental systems is still on-going at the time of writing. Through General Meyer, Marshall had a dramatic effect on the Army of the 1980s which promised to continue well into the 21st century.

Whether the post-Vietnam generation of junior officers will draw as heavily on Marshall's ideas as the post-World War II generation did, or whether his influence will gradually die out because Marshall is no longer available to advocate his views is difficult to say. Many of his innovations have already been incorporated into basic doctrine and are steadily used and modified to meet the changes in technology and requirements of modern warfare. As these and similar innovations take root in the future, Marshall's efforts will not have been in vain.

1. For example, although the 44th Military History Detachment does not use the group interview technique, its members are aware of it and have consciously chosen not to use it.

2. Marshall, *Bringing Up the Rear*, p. 203.

3. Furthermore, though not directly related to his influence on the military, his focus on the subject of combat at the soldier's level affected the way subsequent authors wrote military history. According to Dr. John Westover, "Marshall had another great impact—that on military literature. His own accounts set a standard for combat stories and often provided the information itself. The interview materials developed by the combat historians were not private property but public domain. Quite a number of popular historians mined those accounts. One of the most successful was Cornelius Ryan's *The Longest Day*. Marshall's own story of *Pork Chop Hill* became a successful movie." Letter from Dr. John Westover to the author, August 9, 1983.

4. In the early 1970s, Kinton, Inc., was charged with helping the Army Research Institute develop an improved training system for small units. The result was a program still in use—Realtrain. The after-action review became an integral part of the system, and Marshall collaborated on its use. See Edgar L. Shriver, et al., "Technical Report S-4, Realtrain: A New Method for Tactical Training of Small Units," Army Research Institute, December 1975, found in the MC.

5. Conversations with Dr. Gregory Belenke in August 1983, and on the telephone March 6, 1984. As an example, an as yet unpublished article entitled "The Combat Stress Threat," by Peyton R. Williams, Jr., WRAIR's Foreign Science Information Officer, referred to *Night Drop* for proof that unit cohesion enhances the individual's ability to reduce stress and that the psychological stress arising from uncertainty contributes to physical stress.

6. Marshall, *Bringing Up the Rear*, p. 244.

7. Letter from Joseph Coates, Institute for Defense Analysis, to Marshall, December 18, 1963; also letter from Captain Calvin P. Kennedy, 18th Military History Detachment, 25th Infantry Division, to Marshall, February 23, 1967, both in the MC.

8. From a xerox of a report produced by Kinton, Incorporated, in conjunction with the Army Research Institute, entitled, "Technical Report S-4, Realtrain: A New Method for Tactical Training of Small Units," by Edgar L. Shriver, et al., December 1975, found in the MC.

9. Paul R. Bleda, "Realtrain: A Critique," *Army*, November 1978, pp. 35-37.

10. General Meyer was the first Chief of Staff to use video tapes to make his presence felt by all the leaders in the Army. He made several which stressed the importance of small unit leadership and how his programs were designed to enhance those principles. Every officer in the Army was required to view those tapes.

*Marshall giving a briefing while assigned to the
Information Branch, Special Service Division in 1942 or 1943.*

Marshall and Westover in Bastogne.

Marshall with Lt Bill Fox in Bastogne.

Marshall in the field in Brittany, circa 1944.

Courtesy John G. Westover

Enlisted and civilian personnel of the Historical Section at work.

Courtesy Marshall Collection

Marshall interviewing a group of infantrymen, Normandy, August 1944.

Courtesy Marshall Collection

Marshall compiling interview notes, Normandy, 1944.

Courtesy John G. Westover

Marshall receiving the Legion of Merit, presented to him by Col W.A. Ganoe, Theater Historian ETO, 3 April 1945.

US Army photo
Courtesy John G. Westover

Marshall at a 7th Infantry Division outpost, Korea, April 1953.

*General S.L.A. Marshall, author of AMBUSH, at work in the
field in Vietnam after interviews.*

Marshall with Lt Gen Stanley R. Larson, CG, 1st Field Force, and Brig Gen Willard Pearson, CG, 1st Bde, 101st Airborne Division, Vietnam, 1966 or 1967.

APPENDIX A

HEADQUARTERS
EUROPEAN THEATER OF OPERATIONS
UNITED STATES ARMY
APO 887

26 June 1944

MEMORANDUM

TO :   The members of the Historical Teams

SUBJECT :   Methods of interviews based on success of Lt. Col. S.L.A. Marshall in the Pacific

1. I have asked Colonel Marshall, who has returned from the Pacific and is here as representative of the War Department, whose previous letters most of us have read, to put out for our aid a concrete summation of methods used successfully by him in interviews with small units or front-line troops.

2. The following is the result of his work to that end. Not only do I regard it as masterful but most extraordinarily helpful to all of us. On the other hand let me caution you to adapt the methods herein disclosed to your personality. The principles certainly are not inviolable.

COMPANY INTERVIEW AFTER COMBAT
Lt. Col. S.L.A. Marshall, Inf.

Nature of Company Interview After Combat

Company interviews are, in essence, a detailed recording of the complete company experience during a sustained action or through an episode which is significantly related to a larger action. They are the means, finally, of rounding out the battle history of the regiment and the division and of closing up the gaps in a narrative which might be drawn from the organizational journals and orders. When a company had fought a pivotal or a particularly obscure action, when one would otherwise have to use the word "confused" in referring to its share in the action as a whole, or when its contribution to the general battle was of such decisive and outstanding importance that its role stands above all others and is therefore deserving of the most minute searching so that the battle history may be organized with balance and perspective, there is need for a company interview after combat. Once the Historical Officer ascertains that a company experience within a particular general action calls for such special treatment, he should proceed to his mission at the earliest opportunity, according to the availability of the company and the willingness of the Divisional and Regimental Commands. It will be found that after Division gives its sanction to the process and passes on to the Regimental Commander its desire that the Regiment cooperate, an expression by the Regimental Commander will be sufficient to assure the required action and attitude on the part of the company.

When the Interview Should Be Sought

What one learns by examining the Regimental and Battalion journals, supplemented by what one hears from Staff Officers, or Commanders, or for that matter from any other personnel either in extension or in explanation of the records or in casual comment on a battle which is being fought or has been fought, provide the keys to the Historical Officer's estimation of when a detailed inquiry into small unit action is required. To cite a few examples: One examines the journal and finds that company B of the --- Regiment captured Hill 250 and reported the loss of 87 men. The losses elsewhere in the Regiment on that day are relatively light. Yet the Battalion had been in check in front of this position for two days, and immediately after capturing it, was able to press on at a rapid rate. Inquiry from Division G-3 or Regiment S-3, or for that matter, from other sections of either staff, may elicit the information that the effect was decisive for the time being and that Company B bore the brunt of a fight which resulted in a general retirement by the enemy force. It is not likely to yield more than that. An heroic small unit action deserving of five thousand words may be compressed in the journal to four or five typewritten lines. The Historical Officer then makes note that company B's capture of Hill 250 is a proper subject for a company interview. He then seeks the first opportunity to close the interview, his own dispositions and the convenience of the company considered. If the Battalion has been in the lines for some days, it may already have returned to a reserve position. Men do not ordinarily object to being interviewed about their battle experience at this time; in fact, they relish it. It comes as a relief and as partial recognition to them. Companies have been interviewed in this manner within 30 minutes after leaving the front and their Battalion officers have participated willingly. To cite another example: In going over the journal and in discussing it with the Battalion Executive or S-3, or with members of a Regimental Staff, the Historical Officer may hear it said: "Company F got into a bad situation there and was badly mauled. We don't know in detail what happened to it. They got out-flanked and lost one platoon but they managed to hold their ground. They at first told us that they would have to retire." That is a signal to the HO of a situation which calls for special inquiry. Confusion almost invariably attends any attack by the enemy upon our defensive position, especially when it occurs at night and where our losses are acute. That is true, also, where our forces encounter enemy strength where they have least expected to find it. Under these circumstances, the combat organizations do not have the resources for a detailed inquiry into what happened. The record and the regimental knowledge will usually be cognizant only of the result. Yet such episodes are a most fertile field for the HO's searching (1) Because the Regiment is usually as anxious to know what happened as is the HO, and (2) Because such actions are especially relevant of small unit character and of what happens to our soldiery under conditions of unusual stress. The most vital battle stuff to be had for the furtherance of history and of military knowledge comes of careful inquiry into such experience.

Value and Analysis of Company Evidence

The theory of the Company Interview After Combat is based upon three fundamental propositions (1) That every eyewitness has a part of the story (2) That a number of eye-witnesses and the cross-checking of their experience is invariably more valid than the dogmatic assertions of any one witness (3) That it is the position of the witness with reference to the action under inquiry and his ability to tell his story of what he saw, heard, felt and said which determines the value of his evidence. Relative rank does not bear on the weight of the evidence as to what matured during the fire fight. A man knows best what he saw happen right around him and in the main, he is not likely to be mistaken as to his role in the combat, especially if there are others with him who can confirm and supplement his story, or on the other hand, correct him if he deviates from the straight line of truth. Hearsay evidence (what one man heard another man say as to what happened to some other element of the unit) is rarely to be used. There is one general exception to this rule: One must take the word of a living man for what their dead or badly wounded comrades did and said, as it will be found almost unexceptionably that they played a conspicuous part in the action and that the living are especially concerned with being exact in relating what befell them. The word of a superior as to what a detail or a man did should not be allowed to prevail against the direct testimony of the man himself, provided it is supported by the circumstances or by the evidence of other witnesses. It will be found that company officers invariably accept such statements as correct and valid even where they are corrective of the officer's own concept of the situation.

Preparation for Interview of Company

The progress of the interview, and in fact its whole concept, is according to the nature of battle. Here again there are two fundamental truths to be considered: (1) It is never the case that all elements of a company are actually engaged at one time though all may be present, and (2) Battle is never a maelstrom into which all are drawn equally, but is rather a continuing line of small eddies which are sometimes tactically related and sometimes not. The thing to do is to find the starting point—the point where some element of the company first fires upon the enemy or is fired on by him in the action under inquiry—and then develop that episode and all subsequent episodes in chronological order and in relation to one another. This starting point should be determined before ever the company is assembled by inquiry among the company officers and platoon noncoms. That is a part of the briefing process before the HO is fully prepared to develop the company narrative. The HO should inform himself fully on how the company action is related to the general battle and the movements of the regiment. He can get this regimental view of the matter from the Regimental Staff or Command. If possible, he should also get the Battalion view of the action—what the company did with relation to the other companies of the Battalion—from that Headquarters. He should also familiarize himself with the ground over which the action was fought, either by going over it in detail or by map study. In other words, he should know the larger significance of what the company accomplished more fully than the company itself knows. This sounds difficult, but is extremely easy, since combat companies have invariably only a local knowledge of their achievements. Armed with this information, he is then in the proper position to appear before the company, since then he can relate all that he hears to the context of the battle, without having to be led around by the hand by the company. Having so prepared himself, he is ready to proceed to the interview.

How the Interview Is Carried Forward

The company is assembled. All of the company officers should be present. It is desirable that the Battalion S3 and S2, and either the Commander or his Executive also be present, and when they understand what is sought, they are usually more than willing to accommodate. The HO already knows the starting point of the action. He has pegged down two or three witnesses, perhaps the Company Commander, or the leader of one of the platoons, or the non-com in charge of the group which first engaged. The HO explains the reasons for the assembly. He tells them something of this sort: "What you did is considered of sufficient importance that the Army believes it should be a part of recorded history. We are here today to determine the facts. It is your duty to relate what you know of them to the best of your ability, holding nothing back and exaggerating nothing. Here, you are all equal as witnesses. For the time being, we all stand on the same ground. If you hear any man present, whatever his rank, say something which you think to be incorrect or which you feel requires some additional information, it is your duty to stand up and speak your piece. If you hear me make a statement which you feel is a faulty interpretation of your action, you should be quick to stand up and call it to my attention. If it occurs to you that I am missing an important line of inquiry in trying to develop your story, you will be doing the Army and the country a service to tell me so out loud. Whatever you say, speak audibly so that all present will hear you: That will help them to remember and will encourage them to participate. Your commanders are desirous that you should tell your part in the battle as fully and as frankly as possible. It is not the time to be modest about it. What is learned here today may help save the lives of other American soldiers or add to your own company efficiency. Such vital information has come out of these company interviews before this, and it may well happen here today." The HO then calls his first witness. As this witness brings in the names of other men, they should be called upon to add their bit of information about the opening incident. This helps break the ice. The opening of the interview is also a propitious time to call on the platoon leaders to describe the ground over which the action was fought. After they have described it, the men as a whole are asked to add whatever details of ground are within their recollection. This subject should be developed fully at the beginning of the interview not only because of its significance but because it is the easiest way to get the men talking freely. After the dam once breaks and they become interested participants, the interview will carry itself so long as the HO continues to guide it along the main channel of the action.

Unit Leaders May Take Lead in Interview

There is no need that the HO do all of the questioning. Indeed, it is desirable and beneficial for the Company Commander to lead the discussion where he is willing to do so. Or for that matter, if the Company action breaks down tactically into platoon action, it is desirable to put a fluent and able platoon commander in front of the body of his men and let him take the leading hand in developing the narrative. Where the platoon actions are quite distinct and the men have not become inter-mixed, it is often advantageous to work with one platoon at a time, completing each platoon narrative, and then recomposing the company narrative as a whole after dovetailing the incidents of the different platoons. When the unit leaders appear in this role, the HO stands forward with the officer who is doing the questioning. He keeps his mind on the context of the narrative as it is being developed to make certain that all of the parts are presented in proportion. He may either supplement the work of the chief interrogator by asking questions directly of the company or by feeding his questions to the interrogator. He must look constantly for cause and effect. It is not enough to know that men fell back; there must be a reason for their falling back. It is not enough to know that a squad went forward. How did it go forward? Did it rush, or did it crawl? It is not enough to record that 10 men fell at a given place. What was the nature of the fire delivered against them? What effect did the casualties have upon those around them? How were the men re-grouped on the ground where they fell? It is not enough to know that at a given time, the Commander put his 60 mm mortars into action. What were the targets? Over what distance did the fire range? What were the observed results? How many rounds did the mortar section fire? It is not enough to ask at what time troops landed at a given point. Did they land wet or dry? Did they lose any equipment on landing? Did they go to ground immediately? How did they feel while they were pinned down by fire? It is not enough to ask what kind of radio or other communications facility the company had. Did it work? How well did it work? When was it supplemented by runners? If communication failed, why did it fail? It is not enough to determine, in connection with a local episode, that M-1s and grenades were used. How many men actually fired with the M-1s or threw grenades? Answers can be had with a showing of hands. The list of types of questions and of their amplifications is almost endless. The object of the search is to make certain that every vital point is covered. In line with this objective, no scrap of evidence is too small to be disregarded at the time of inquiry. It is often found that the key to all that occurred may be some fact known to only two or three members of the company and which they themselves considered to be of minor import. The thing to be done is to explore fully every lead stated by any of the witnesses.

Use of Blackboard Required in Interview

The mechanics of the interview are these: There should always be a blackboard, or lacking it, a wall with a piece of chalk at hand, or lacking both, a plot of sand or of clean dirt on which the witnesses can plot their position with relation to the action under inquiry. In the beginning, the Company Commander, or a junior officer or one of the sergeants is asked to make a rough sketch of the general position. There will usually be any number of men willing to volunteer for this duty. Then as other participants relate of their action, they are requested to come forward to the blackboard or wall and place themselves on the map. As this sketch develops, or more suitably, after the action is complete and all of the details have been added to it, the HO should make a small copy of it which is later appended to the narrative. This is SOP, as without the sketch, the narrative will not become cogent and readily understandable. Further, IT MUST BE DONE AT THE TIME, and not from the HO's memory of the sketch.

How the Interview Is Organized in Detail

The basic narrative is constructed out loud in the presence of the company. For this, the HO needs the assistance of one man, at a typewriter, or one man, writing in longhand. It is not necessary to have a stenographer who can take shorthand; the interview does not proceed at a speed which requires it. The HO may call on his own non-com to do this work. Or, when possible, he may get the assistance of a company clerk or one from Battalion or Regimental Headquarters. The most satisfactory routine is to dictate out loud one fact at a time as soon as each fact is clearly developed. For example, a sergeant is relating the action of his group. He says: "I had 10 men with me and when we started forward we had no exact idea where the enemy gun was located. There was a small thicket ahead of us about 60 yards. We advanced to this thicket by bounds, using shell holes and other cover, two men moving out at a time. We received no fire during this advance." Having obtained that much information, the HO does not wait until he learns what matured after the men got to the woods. He has one fact in his grasp; if he tries to get more than that, he will not be able to remember clearly everything that the witness said and his dictating to his assistant will become halting and confused, he will have to ask the witness to repeat, and the men of the company will lose interest in the proceedings. He therefore asks the sergeant to hold it for a minute and he dictates out loud the gist of what he has heard. He does not have to repeat everything the witness has said as oftentimes the witness will include details which are irrelevant and immaterial. For example, if the sergeant in the continuity related above has said: "Thompson and I left off, Smith and Jackson followed, George and White came after that, " there would be no purpose in putting this into the record, since the advance was uneventful and all men reached the first objective. It would be found as a usual thing, however, that the men themselves have a correct sense of what is pertinent and vital and they do not tend to introduce extraneous facts. However, one word of caution should be given on this point. The record is supposed to be warm and human, since an army is a living, and not a mechanical, organism. It is as important to gather the facts on the moral side of war as on the purely physical side. Only so will the record be made to reveal the human nature of our Army. Suppose the sergeant said: "When we got to that thicket, the men were pretty badly worn out. They didn't want to go on and said so. So I told them to hold it for a few minutes and take a smoke, figuring that would steady them," then all that he said would be pertinent to the record. The fact that men are munching on food or shooting crap at the moment when put under counterattack would be more revealing of their lack of anticipation of any danger than any such statement as: "We thought the front was quiet and we weren't prepared for them when they came over."

Attitude and Rules in Conducting Interview

The attitude which the HO can most profitably maintain in front of the company is one of warm interest and respectful attention. He cannot obtain the interest of the company and its complete participation in the work at hand unless he conducts himself as a student rather than a teacher. He must act at all times as if he is hungry for information, and equally, as if all information given him is of consequence. He must remain keen. No matter how difficult it is to draw out the facts, he must not appear discouraged. Men vary from company to company, largely according to their relationship with their immediate superiors. In some cases, it is possible to establish a congenial atmosphere, conducive of frankness and interest, within 10 minutes of the start of the interview. In other cases, the HO may have to work patiently with the company for a day or more before the "dam breaks" and the witnesses participate freely. If he talks offhand with some of the men in between the company assemblies, it will be useful in breaking down their reserve. To reconstruct one day of battle via the company interview method may require anywhere from one to three days of steady work. The following general rules on the conducting of the interview will contribute substantially to the success of the technique:

(1) All witnesses are equal at the time of the interview, the all-encompassing object being to arrive at the truth.

(2) All statements of all witnesses and all statements by the interviewing officer should be audible to all present.

(3) The record should not be regarded as closed at any time. If upon being given time to refresh his memory on an incident which has already been recorded, and witness says that he recalls some new and vital fact, the record should be amended.

(4) The interviewing officer should never cut any witness short or look his disbelief at any statement. If the witness rambles on, a polite way should be found to terminate his statement. For example: "Bring that up with me after the

session!" or "That's not right on the thread of the story, so hold it until a little later." To embarrass any witness will be to freeze many of the others. It is a good idea, always, to thank the witness.

(5) The interviewing officer should be ever ready with his praise. Where a man took a stout part in an action it is always helpful for the HO to commend him in front of the company. "That was well done!" or "That took a lot of guts."

(6) Companies should not be interrogated for longer than 3 hours in any one session. After that, the men tire and interest flags. Three hours in the morning and three in the afternoon is a good day's work.

(7) Be exact as to rank and names. The company clerk should be present with the roster and as each witness appears, he should be completely identified. Say "S/Sgt John J. Smith" not "Sgt Smith." When mentioning companies or platoons in the first instance, say who commanded them.

(8) The interview is not the time for teaching battle lessons. When the witness freely states that which proves that he made a mistake in combat, he should be treated objectively, not to say sympathetically. For any officer to take advantage of his honesty by attempting to point a moral lesson in front of the other men will defeat all of the purposes of the interview.

(9) The narrative should be complete. There should be no blank spots in the report of the action unless all participants are dead. When the narrative bogs down at any point, and around a particular episode, it is advisable to attempt to develop the subject further by exploring it from a fresh angle.

(10) The HO should check back to Battalion on any points concerning the company's action in relation to some other company; he should check back to other arms and units, wherever possible for verification of any statement made with respect to any other arm or unit. Such statements as "We were fired into by our own artillery," or "We were hit by our own mortars" must be handled with extreme discretion. In many cases, this is mere supposition. Unless the point can be competently established, it should not go into the record.

(11) Above all the interviewer must remember he is there to get the facts. He is not conducting a critique, takes no part in tactical debate or becomes personal or emotional. He avoids any reflection on individuals as he would the plague.

3. I know you will be glad to have the above, which I know would be very helpful to me if I were out there too.

4. Will you PLEASE send INFORMAL REPORTS to me as if you were writing home. The best two so far have been from Lt. Col. Jones and Major O'Sullivan, and each apologized for his informality. PLEASE write on anything in anyway and the more complete, unpolished and unstudied the better. Human interest touches are especially helpful. Good Luck:

W. A. GANOE
Colonel, G.S.C.
Theater Historian

APPENDIX B

HEADQUARTERS
3D INFORMATION AND HISTORICAL SERVICE
APO 403

9 December 1944

Lt Col S.L.A. Marshall, Deputy Theater Historian
European Theater of Operations
APO 887, U.S. Army

Dear Colonel Marshall,

I am replying to your letter of 1 December, as promised in mine of the fourth.

This letter, or memorandum, is based on personal theories, and on the practical experiences of all members of the 3d Information and Historical Service in the four months during which the Third US Army has been operational. The theory is derived from the study of European military history and the teaching of the same to graduate seminars at the University of Chicago, in which the study of official records and general staff histories was the basis of instruction. This theory, as further developed after exposure to C&GS "doctrine", affected the manner in which we attempted to carry out the wishes of the War Department and the Theater in the Third US Army. Our practical experiences are as particularized and personalized as the theory. The history of Third US Army in many respects is unique in the present war, particularly as to the use of armor, the extent of terrain covered, and the mobility of operations.

It will be noticed that much which follows turns on two questions: (a) at what tactical and organizational levels is coverage desired? (b) what procedure is to be followed in processing the historical materials obtained in Third Army? We have received only fragmentary and conflicting answers to these two basic questions, both from the War Department and the Theater. It is hoped that the information and suggestions proffered herein will be considered, by higher echelons of technical supervision, in the formulation of definite and detailed directives.

X X X X X

Before Third US Army became operational, all personnel were given a copy of a *Battalion Check List* drawn up by me. Experience has shown that we lacked the practical background necessary to fully utilize the details contained therein. It was a case of trying to run before being able to walk. However, the guidance offered by the *Battalion Check List* can now be properly used by our personnel, who have a frame of reference built up over four months of action, and the list is being revised and issued to the members of the detachment, as well as to historical officers in Third US Army units.

On 31 July, the day before the Army became operational, all members of this detachment were given the following specific instructions.

1. Prepare notes so that they are legible and comprehensible to other persons. You are not responsible for putting your notes in a sustained, sequential, preliminary narrative at this time.

2. Since the War Department desires pamphlet material, keep always in mind the possibility of turning at least one action, covered by you, into a semi-formal, preliminary draft narrative.

3. This detachment is responsible not only to the War Department and the Theater, but to the Third US Army as well. This will require as much over-all coverage of the Army's activities as possible, as well as specific and detailed coverage of particular actions or operations which may be used for War Department pamphlets. I will try to cover the general story of command at Army level. You will attempt two types of coverage: (a) a day-to-day summary of what Corps Headquarters considers to be the most important problems or happenings of the day (of necessity this will be brief and tabloid in character); (b) specific and detailed coverage of critical and vital actions by combat units.

4. The detailed coverage of critical actions preferably is to be done at the level of the RCT (whether minus or reinforced) or the Combat Command (in the case of armor). The Army Commander emphasizes the use of combined arms; therefore, cover TDs, separate Tk Bns, supporting Artillery and Engineers, in relation to the RCT or CC. Those arms will have records even more inadequate than those compiled by armored or infantry units. Therefore, your interviews with them will be highly important. (Experience has amply demonstrated both the importance of these supporting arms and the inadequacy of their records.) Concentrate on those Bns and Cos within the RCT or CC which bore the brunt of the action.

5. If you have to make a choice between covering an armored unit and an infantry unit, work on the armor.

6. In general, you may choose the action on which you wish to work. However, inform me before you expend too much time. Occasionally I will make a definite assignment—based on the Army picture in order to give comprehensive coverage. In any case consult the G-3 at Corps or Division.

7. Report to me once a week—this may be done verbally or in writing.

8. Don't worry about the rhetorical level of your stuff or the audience towards which it may be aimed. Prepare your notes at a precise and militarily sophisticated pitch.

(Subsequently, I received verbal instructions to concentrate on "front line" coverage; and, in addition, much was said about company actions. However, these instructions were much too fragmentary and general to be of help to myself or the detachment.)

X X X X X

The instructions cited above were based on a tactical situation which envisaged three corps with nine to eleven divisions (reinforced heavily by Army troops) in a fast moving, wide reaching, scheme of maneuver. To cover this situation five officers and three enlisted men were available, with four quarter tons.

The prescription of the RCT or CC as a nexus for our activities was based on the following factors.

1. We were responsible for the history of the Third US Army. The size of this task could be envisaged by a simple constellation of figures. Third Army would have a frontage up to 500 miles (during the BRITTANY campaign). Its average minimum front (9-11 divisions) would be approximately 60 miles. The average number of RCTs and CCs would be 30. The average number of battalions (including only infantry, TD and Tk Bns) would be 110. The number of combat companies would be astronomical.

2. So far as we could tell from preliminary plans, and from the Army Commander's tactical doctrine, the normal *task force* would be the RCT or CC reinforced or minus. Therefore, the RCT or CC would be the most important tactical unit—from the Army point of view.

3. The best official or general staff histories between 1870 and 1939 had been written with emphasis on the regiment (or brigade) and its component battalions. This was true in the case of the general staff histories written by the Germans on the Boer War, the Russo-Japanese, and the Balkan Wars, (a case comparable to our own since the Germans used only a handful of military observers—better trained than our men, it is true, but without such freedom of access to the troops.) The same emphasis was applied to the World

War I histories—whether compiled from operation and battle reports (German, Austrian, French), or war diaries (British, Canadian), or interlarded with interviews (as in the case of the Australian Official History).

We were well aware that we would not write the official or general staff version of the Third US Army history, but it was believed that we were responsible for obtaining as wide a coverage as possible, so that such an official or general staff study could be made.

4. Finally, it was believed that from an editorial point of view (with which we were indirectly concerned) the RCT or CC would cover a large enough number of individuals to meet the War Department demand for pamphlets directed to as many of the wounded as possible; while at the same time separate RCT or CC stories could be combined editorially as desired into Division or Corps histories.

X X X X X

The following experience data usually divides into two phases, i.e., the initial period of open or maneuver warfare (up to the MOSELLE line), and the subsequent period of closed or relatively stabilized warfare.

Directives and Control. During the early period of Third US Army's operations, control in our detachment was exercised either through personal conversations with the individual officers or in meetings of the entire detachment. Written reports were not required. Subsequently, it was found necessary to insure written directives to the detachment. First, because the individual officer often needed a written order from this headquarters to convince the Corps that he had a job which must be done immediately and which would prevent him from working for the Corps. Secondly, written orders were issued to prevent misunderstanding, since generally it was necessary to set up priorities as to coverage with perhaps half a dozen actions listed. In all cases I carefully reviewed the Army picture before determining what actions should have priority coverage. The Army G-3 has seen a list of these actions and has concurred point by point with the choices made. In addition, the men in the field consulted with Corps and Division G-3s, and received valuable suggestions as to what coverage should be undertaken. (This has been particularly true at Division level.)

Access to Combat Units. During the period of the drive across BRITTANY and FRANCE, the mobility of Third Army operations made prolonged access to combat units very difficult indeed. The units, in most instances, were either fighting or marching, and coverage was catch as catch can. In cases where combat units were committed to siege warfare, as at ST MALO and

METZ, access to the unit involved was much easier. In the present period of combat, the accessibility of units has varied greatly. One division has been in line for 56 days and has been actively engaged in that entire period. Another division, which I am very anxious to cover, fought a series of highly important actions between 8-17 November. From 17 November to 1 December the division fought no important engagement, but was constantly in line or on the move. Beginning 1 December the division commenced a critical three-day action—which is just in the mopping up stages at the moment. Arrangements have been made for a man to go to the division, if another fight does not immediately develop. The division is anxious to have coverage, but has stated categorically that no time, since 8 November, has been suitable for covering any of the units within the division. Now when a man does go to that division, he will have at least two extensive periods of action to cover, one nearly a month old. He will have to make a choice as to which of the two series of actions he wishes to cover and quite probably will not be able to complete either one, since the fights lasted so long and will take much time to cover.

In general, all lower units like to have our historians with them, but tell us quite candidly when, in their opinion, interviewing in inadvisable. This is sometimes carried to extremes by higher headquarters. A Corps Chief of Staff ordered one of my officers to conduct interviews between midnight and four in the morning, which meant, of course, that no interviews could be conducted at all.

Our experience leads to the following conclusions. First, the theory that there are always elements in reserve and thus available to interview is untenable. There have been two reasons for this lack of reserves on the Third Army front: (1) during the period of movement everybody was committed either to fight or to march; (2) during the period of closed warfare it has not been found necessary to keep out tactical reserves because the enemy is not able to offer any large scale and serious threat of counterattack. When a counterattack is sustained, it generally consists of a small force and is repelled, or the lost area is regained, by a regrouping of elements already in the line. I cannot stress too strongly the inadvisability of carrying World War theory on this matter of reserves over into Third Army experience. It is necessary to add that the Army Commander has positively stated his unwillingness to hold out elements for either flank protection or Army reserve. I have noted in an earlier memorandum a case in point where, on one occasion, an armored division was cited in official operations reports as "Army reserve" while in fact all three combat commands were committed piece-meal and actively engaged in combat on the line. When the Third Army slows down it is general in effect and, all at once, we have more units to interview than we have personnel available.

Secondly, our experience has indicated that a big drive cannot be adequately covered while it is going on (and I call attention to the high percentage of our operational history during which we have been engaged in a big drive). During a drive or the mounting of a large-scale attack the following procedure obtains in our detachment. An officer visits a division, regiment or battalion and gets a general picture from informed personnel. From this he makes notes as to what specific actions and what interesting and informative details should be sought for at a later period when the unit (or individual) is available for interview. At the same time these visits to units in combat remind combat personnel that there is an historical officer who will be back later. Also, such visits give invaluable tips as to when a unit may be coming out of the line.

Thirdly, experience has shown that coverage cannot be completed in the case of many actions. The reasons for this follow. Every action worth covering at all requires several days of work by the officer or non-com. In a great many instances, the interviewer gets two days with the unit (where he needs five for completion of the story) and then the unit is recommitted for several days or weeks. When that particular unit is available again the officer may be involved elsewhere with another story and unable to return and complete his coverage. Furthermore, and this factor has become increasingly important, the personnel partially questioned in the first interview may be dead when the unit is again accessible. I realize as well as anyone, I believe, the necessity of obtaining the complete and integrated story of an action. But the periods of rest for units in action are so very brief and the work of coverage by a single officer is of necessity so very slow that again and again we will obtain part of the story, but not all of it. This is unavoidable and I have worked on the premise that half a loaf is better than no bread. There are a great many variations on this. Sergeant Harrison spent five days interviewing personnel of two infantry battalions which had been engaged in an extremely important XV Corps action. Before he could complete his work the XV Corps passed from Third Army control. The Corps G-3 tried to put Sergeant Harrison on the Corps T/O and I had to get him back to Third Army pronto. Sergeant Ludden worked for a long time on a river crossing operation by an RCT (-). The story today is incomplete because an attached Tk Bn, which was vital to the story, was sent to another Army before he could reach it.

However, in both the instances cited we now possess important tactical information which may be used in piecing together the history of the Third

Army—even though we do not possess a complete and comprehensive story of the specific action.

The Mechanics of Interviews. All interviews have been conditioned by the relative military ranks of the interviewer and interviewee. Since nearly all battalion commanders are lieutenant colonels, the approach to a battalion must of necessity be rather different in the case of company grade officers than what you experienced in the Pacific and in Europe. Recently I have arranged for some of my officers to accompany the two Corps Combat Observers, Colonel Webb and Lt. Col. Miller, when they visited regiments and battalions and held interviews. The results are very markedly different than when my officers approach the same units on their own. The two colonels are able to get immediate attention and as a result can do in one-half day what my men estimate would take them two days to do. The two colonels are able to request (i.e., order) that all battalion officers be gathered in one spot or that a platoon be brought together for an interview. This is done immediately and generally without question. The two colonels are able to interrupt a Lt. Col., Bn CO, in the midst of a narrative and keep harassing him until the answers to certain questions are forthcoming.

None of these things can be done with the rank we have at our disposal. My men must wait, sometimes half a day, sometimes two days, before they can talk to the individuals they are after. On only a few occasions have they been able to obtain a mass interview or anything approaching it. If a Lt. Col. commanding a battalion feels that he knows the entire story and is unwilling to let anyone else be brought into the interview there is nothing that my officers can do about it. If a Lt. Col. is in a hurry and unwilling to discuss details, it is impossible for a junior officer to *insist* that he cover those details. (Parenthetically, we are beginning to see some veiled antagonism, traceable to the shortage of company grade officers, and the apparent youth and able-bodied character of our officers.)

I realize fully the importance of determining precisely who is responsible for a given statement of fact. All my people have been told to get the name of the officer making any statement which is quoted directly. However, when a half-dozen officers are gathered around a map and a member of this detachment is attempting to conduct an interview and make notes at the same time (we do not have EM, with the officers, who can take down notes), it becomes well nigh impossible to document every statement of fact, and if this were attempted the interview would grind slowly to a halt. The best that can be done is to put down the names of all officers at the interview and present what is their consensus, noting the name of a specific officer only when he is quoted verbatim or when there are variations of opinion.

The weather is now playing a vital part in determining what form our interviews will take. A tank battalion, for example, bivouacked in a town or spread out over two or three little villages, as is often the case, should not be brought together for an interview in this weather. Members of that battalion may have to walk one or two miles to a central meeting place through mud and cold. I have given strict instructions that no one is to keep any GI or officer, no matter how willing, in the cold or mud when the officer or man has just come out of the line. In circumstances such as this our men must act as Fuller brush salesmen and go from door to door, that is, from shed to shed and house to house, talking to little groups of men or officers billeted here and there.

Maintenance has become a terrific problem with our Army. Orders taking armored units out of the line now read "It is ordered that the —— Tk Bn be relieved for 24 hours of rest and "maintenance." Experience shows that there is little rest but a great deal of maintenance. At such a time the battalion officers occasionally are available for interview, but the individual platoon leader or tank commander is down supervising work on the vehicle and usually not available for interview.

At the present time our technique has evolved to this stage. After getting general information from the divisional and regimental level, generally by talking to only one or two officers in those echelons, we go to the battalion CO and request an interview. The Bn CO usually calls in his Ex O, his S-3, and his company COs; that is, those who are still alive. Platoon leaders are brought in when available. The battalion CO pretty well determines who will be at the interview, although my officers are all instructed to ask for the important members of the battalion staff and company and platoon commanders. Occasionally we run across a battalion commander who thinks that he knows the entire story and does not wish any intervention from his other officers. In such a case we obtain his story and attempt to work from the battalion indirectly and pick up a company CO here and there. Such a process, however, takes a great deal of time, and since the battalion CO is a little king, this is a devious practice which we avoid.

The battalion, incidentally, is harder for the non-com than is the regiment or even the division. An assistant G-3 at division will talk more readily to a non-com than will a battalion S-3.

In the METZ area we found that given two or three days for interviewing, which was often the maximum, we could get more *precise* information and wider coverage on an action from interviews with the battalion staff, company

116

commanders and platoon leaders than we could by interviewing the rank and file of a company. It should be noted, moreover, that a regimental or battalion staff is relatively accessible since they are all together in a shed or a tank park, while the members of a company, and this is particularly true of armor, may be spread over considerable distances. Furthermore, battalion officers, and this is even more true of regimental officers, can be talked to in the evening when, because of early darkness and the dispersal of troops in forward areas, it is impossible to get to the GIs. Finally a good battalion S-3 knows more about the *important* events of an action than does the platoon or the company commander. The battalion staff is quite as much in the line, in most cases, as the company grade officers, but with greater opportunities for observation.

Terrain Study. Our study of terrain has had two phases. In the first phase, we rolled over hundreds of miles in a jeep trying to keep up with the fast-moving elements of Third Army. We saw considerable terrain *en gros*, but did not have the opportunity to study it closely. It was my thought that at the cessation of hostilities the men who had covered a particularly important action would go back, with their interviews and documents, and make a detailed study of the terrain.

In the second phase, that is, the period of closed warfare, our personnel has had greater opportunity to study the ground and is so doing. However, it has been impossible to retrace a unit action on the ground in company with members of that unit. The time lag between our coverage of an action and the action itself means that the unit has moved off the ground on which the action was fought by the time the interview takes place.

Our procedure, therefore, is to conduct interviews with maps and have the officers interviewed indicate on the map the course of the action. The resultant inaccuracies are exactly what should be expected. No matter what the scale of the map the individual tends to be inexact and uncertain when he is pressed for detailed locations or paths of movement. If he could be returned to the terrain, obviously the results would be better. Given the conditions under which we have operated, I have come to view with skepticism any maps or overlays which give the specific and exact location and movements of individual tanks, artillery pieces, or machine guns. Of course, we can place these items on an overlay or a map, but we are dealing with approximations of the truth. Theoretically, it should be possible to trace the movements of a platoon of tanks during an action. Practically, one only has to look at the maze of armored tracks on a hill where a tank platoon has been engaged to know that exactness as to movement is impossible. I have come to trust *area* location and movement of units only. In summation, with very few exceptions, I do not trust exact and pin-point locations of either individuals or weapons.

Maps. The Third Army does not work on maps of 1/10,000 and 1/12,500 scale even at the lowest level. Armor usually works on 1/100,000 and maps of this scale ordinarily are carried in the individual tanks. Infantry works on 1/50,000 and 1/25,000, although the lower elements of one of our divisions prefer to work on 1/100,000. Neither I nor my officers have seen any maps of 1/10,000 or 1/12,500 in the hands of troops, except for ST MALO, METZ and selected coverage along the RHINE River. During interviews battalion and company officers prefer to work on the 1/50,000 and 1/25,000, and it is my opinion that these are the best scales for our work. Incidentally, some of our most important actions were fought with no maps available to troops but the Michelin road maps (1/200,000).

Overlays and Sketches. The practice of using acetate makes any collection of sequential overlays extremely difficult. During actual combat it is very difficult for my officers to crowd in around the single S-3 map in a regimental or battalion CP, generally set up in a small shed or one CP tent, and make an overlay of the piece of acetate on the map. If, as in most cases, we arrive days after an action, the opportunity to obtain an overlay is gone. The best solution to this problem is to try, as we have tried, to educate divisional and regimental staffs in the necessity of completing and saving overlays for the important phases of important actions.

We do not have enough personnel to take the time to make a whole series of overlays from existing overlays at battalion or regimental level. Therefore, we follow the practice of making our own overlays in interviews and relying as well upon the overlay which the unit will send in attached to its after action report or supporting documents. This is not the best solution, but it is the practical one. My officers have been told specifically not to request overlays from a willing S-3 if it means that the overlay will be taken out of the records and not forwarded through official channels.

We have not done as well on sketch maps as we might have. Steps are being taken to correct this omission and increased access to terrain will mean that our sketches should be much better in the future. However, any sketch or overlay will look 1000% better if a real draftsman does the job. We have no draftsmen.

Photos. For our purpose oblique air cover is the best photo coverage available. Air flies vertical rather than oblique coverage in a large percentage of cases. However, we always attempt to obtain copies of both vertical and oblique photos. Negatives of such photos are filed religiously by the Air-3, at

Army, and by the signal detachments at Army and XIX TAC, but, obviously, these negatives are not available to us at this time. We can only hope to obtain a positive picture now and thus be prepared to ask for a specific, numbered negative when it is needed for production purposes. The one certain method by which we can obtain negatives is to take the pictures ourselves. At the present time this detachment has two cameras—one of which does not work.

Reliability of Evidence. For several years at the University of Chicago another professor and myself offered a course on "Historical Method" in which we examined the rules of historical evidence. Experience with the Third Army has been most interesting, since one is seldom able to deal with oral testimony at the academic level. However, I find that the established rules of historical proof and the *Lehrbuch* apply 100% in the type of work on which the detachment is engaged.

We do not meet positive and flagrant attempts to mislead. At Army Headquarters I have not been able to detect a single attempt at falsification or misrepresentation. We have found only two obvious and demonstrable cases of misrepresentation at lower levels. But there have been many cases, in lower units, where we have been confronted with evasive or negative replies to embarrassing questions.

I do not belong to the "futilitarian" school of history which believes that it is impossible to arrive at the truth. However, my experience and that of my detachment forces me to conclude that truth in war is even more relative that truth in other fields of human action. I have stated above why I distrust pinpoint identifications in any constellation of men, materiel and terrain. As you know from experience, the time lag between an action and interviews with individuals engaged in that action may result in a very considerable, yet unconscious deviation from the facts as known at the time of the action. For the reasons cited above, we seldom are able to reach a unit sooner than a week to 10 days after the action which we wish to study. (Often the time lag is much greater.) In a week's time a unit has developed a mental "set" which may result in a very gratifying unanimity of opinion when the unit is interviewed, but which unanimity of opinion, when analyzed, is a "story agreed upon" or a thesis which has been developed by the commanding or dominant personality of the group (the man with the loudest voice at the mess table) and which has been accepted, quite unconsciously, by the unit. We have a rule of thumb that no testimony is to be accepted until at least two individuals have been interviewed on the same subject. However, it is my conclusion that the best ultimate check will be to square the interviews against the message files and the journals kept by the unit during the hours of the action. (I except after action reports. Those I have seen have all been "edited." But nobody will bother to edit message files and journals—it is too much trouble.)

There is still another reason why I am skeptical of whole-hearted reliance on verbal testimony, as we are forced to collect such verbal testimony in the Third Army. You will realize from your own experience that the problem of collecting evidence differs when a unit is interviewed after one action or a brief series of fights, no matter how bitter and bloody, and when a unit has fought a long series of sustained engagements with no period of rest intervening. A unit that has been 30-40 days in the line comes out "punchy" and with the memory of all but the most recent events considerably dimmed. One of my officers was told by a Bn Commander in an armored outfit: "I want to help you and I'm anxious that you get the true story, but I find that I just cannot remember. I live in 12-hour periods and my mind has come to concern itself only with the 12-hour period in which I exist."

Unfortunately, the action in which we are most interested may have occurred 20 days before the unit comes out of line and the resultant testimony thus becomes more unreliable than in the case of lesser actions which have just occurred and in which we have little interest.

Two very important considerations have to be applied to all our verbal evidence. First, practically everybody from the Army commander on down has a certain "tendency" in his own interpretation or recital of facts. This tendency may be in dislike of some personality in higher echelons of command, or it may be a prejudice against or a predisposition towards a particular weapon. In the second place, we have found that few units will admit to having received any real support from neighboring or attached units, particularly if another arm is involved, but will seek to place blame for failures on such neighboring or attached units. For example, infantry testimony on armor is suspect.

In summary, I would say that oral testimony, as we have gathered it, increases the body of knowledge about the Third Army, but should never be considered definitive.

Tactical Levels of Coverage. Both my detachment and myself believe that the best unit coverage is at the level of the RCT or CC. Of course my detachment may be prejudiced by the direction I gave their thinking before Third Army operations began. However, there are reasons of experience for my continued adherence to this theory. Tactical control in its most illuminating form is exercised at the level of the RCT or the CC. This has been true throughout most of Third Army's history. It will be even more so as the Third Army moves against the SIEGFRIED LINE and the RHINE River. A few days ago one of the Corps stated in an operations order that operations directives and assignment of objectives would be given directly to RCTs and CCs.

Not only is control exercised at this level, but here is found the use of combined arms. A great deal of lip service is given to the doctrine of combined arms, but I suspect that history will fail to record the use, both good and bad, of combined arms, if there is single-minded concentration on either infantry or armor. For example, the Third Army has fought many river crossing actions. These river crossing actions have turned on small task forces comprised of 2 or 3 Bns of Inf, 1 Tk Bn and/or 1 TD Bn, plus Engrs, plus Arty preparation or direct support, plus Air. It would be possible to concentrate on the coverage of the Inf Cos involved in such crossings, but to do so would result in a distortion of the tactical fact and a perversion of the historical truth. Time and time again a separate Tk Bn or a couple of Cos of Tds have turned the tide for such task force operations. Yet on the other hand, to cover the tanks or TDs alone, in a "small unit action," also would lead to distortion and certainly would give a very fragmentary and false picture. To cover these task forces (generally RCTs or CCs) requires time. Sergeant Harrison, who in spite of his non-com status, is one of the fastest and most adroit interviewers we have, spent approximately two weeks covering 1 Tk Bn, 1 TD Bn, and 2 Cos of Armd Inf—and still has coverage of other armored units to make before he can be said to have a well rounded, complete, and self-sustained tactical story of one week of action. Sergeant Angulo spent two weeks covering just the Arty, Engr, TD and Tk Bn aspects of a river crossing by an RCT. But without such coverage Lieutenant Burts' material on the regiment involved would have been historically untrue.

I wish to stress this problem of combined arms. Arty is a case in point. Unfortunately, we do not have time to get all I would like on Arty. Indeed, we have only one series of interviews on an Arty action. Arty records are notoriously incomplete and give little besides the number of rounds fired, the time, and the coordinates on which fire was directed. The results of fire are almost always stated in indefinite terms and practically never does an Arty unit give the slightest indication as to what friendly units required fire and what, specifically, was the target. The Third Army relies heavily upon its artillery and its superiority in that arm. We have had cases where infantrymen prepared to fire small arms at enemy elements attacking in strength only to see the enemy cut down by indirect artillery fire before the MGs and rifles could be brought to bear. The same sort of close coordination, reminiscent of the highly developed 1917 infantry-artillery team, is familiar in our river crossing operations. This is particularly true now that bad weather has set in.

What I have said about artillery can be repeated for the TDs and separate Tk Bns. When we begin to operate with a focal point lower than the RCT or CC we are certain to miss or distort the role of combined arms.

The CC or RCT seems to me to be the focal point not only because it is the center of tactical control and presents the best picture of combined arms at lower levels, but also because we can get something approaching adequate coverage of the Army by following the RCTs and CCs. Of course, it is admitted that we can never get complete coverage on every important action by each RCT or CC! We can hope (particularly with the addition of new personnel to this detachment) to get enough complete or partially complete actions of RCTs or CCs to give us some good solid rocks around which to place the mortar when we obtain the written records.

I wish to make clear that our emphasis on the RCT or CC does not mean that we concern ourselves only with regimental staffs. In order to understand what the RCT or CC is doing it is necessary to go to the next lower tactical level, that is, the Bn, and there obtain the testimony of Bn Commanders, Bn staff, and Co and Plat leaders. I do not believe it is possible to go lower than that and trace the activities of the individual soldier or his squad unless we are prepared to accept a hit and miss story of the Third Army. But whenever it is possible to follow the individual soldier, as an important, decisive and colorful part of the story, and without detracting from our main effect, we do so.

Conclusion. I have set forth above some conclusions derived from our experiences. However, it is not in my province to determine policy. I have layed down a tentative procedure as to level of coverage and the manner in which materials will be handled in the absence of precise and detailed instructions from the War Department and the Theater. This long memorandum, which I am putting in your hands, is written primarily in hope that we will receive such instructions from higher authority, better aware of the desires of the War Department and authorities in this Theater than we can be.

Is it desired that we do spot coverage of selected units in the Third Army in the sort of detail which could be used in instruction at the Company Officers Course at Fort Benning? Or is it desired that we do coverage which could be used for instructional purposes in the Bn Officers Course at Fort Benning and the General Staff Course at the C & GSS? There is a considerable difference between the levels of instruction in these two instances just mentioned. And there is as great a degree of difference between the types of coverage which may be done in the Third Army. Let me state this another way. Is it desired that we aim towards the optimum of a sustained, sequential and comprehensive narrative of the Third Army's operations, in which narrative we trace in considerable detail what is done by the RCTs, CCs, and their component Bns, but with less emphasis on the Co and Plat, and only incidental reference to the squad and the individual soldier? Or is it desired that we operate at company level and prepare a series of self-contained studies which can be used for "Battle Experiences" and instruction in infantry tactics at the company level? The latter would contribute very little to the development of a comprehensive and properly weighted narrative of the Third Army's operations or of the operations of any of its major component parts.

Our detachment can operate at either level. However, now is the time to issue a directive, if a change from our present procedure is envisaged, because of the fact that we are adding new personnel and because the Army is entering upon a new operational phase.

At the beginning of this memorandum I mentioned two questions which are of important and pressing concern to my people and myself. The first question I have asked in the paragraphs above. The second question turns on the processing and preparation of the raw materials which we are securing. In your letter of 30 November, subject: "Handling of Material", you write "So as to insure that the material forwarded to this office will be given the maximum utility and most accurate handling, it is requested that ....". We have received no directive, either written or verbal, as to forwarding materials to any higher echelon. The materials we have shown Colonel Ganoe and yourself have been sent in only as a matter of interest. We would appreciate a directive (which may have already been issued, but never received here) stating exactly what is desired as to the forwarding of materials—particularly those of which we have only one copy—to your office.

This raises the problem as to the writing of pamphlets, monographs, etc., from our collected materials. At the present time I have instructed all personnel to record interviews and transcribe their notes into usable form, but not to take time out to put the unit interviews into a preliminary narrative. Is it desired that the notes on our interviews be prepared in a preliminary narrative and submitted to your office—with the understanding that time may be taken from interviews at night under billeting conditions now common at Division CPs, and I believe that it is impossible to write preliminary narratives in such circumstances.

I would thoroughly disapprove of the idea of a writing staff back in Paris or Washington which will take our interviews and the unit records and compile a final manuscript therefrom. I do not mean that all of my detachment can write—far from it. But I do believe that the best product would be obtained if men who had at least a bowing acquaintance with the ground, the units, the individuals, and the particular problems of Third Army history were given the opportunity to study the records and prepare a rough draft narrative—even if this draft required very considerable editorial revision at higher echelons. There are three men in this detachment who, I believe, should work on anything which is presented to the Army Commander as a product of the labors of this detachment. Captain Clark, Sergeant Harrison, and myself. In addition, we have put in a requisition for a Lieutenant Dunkerley, who has been writing the Army G-2 history. If new personnel is to be added for writing at higher headquarters, I suggest that we be given added personnel for field work and be allowed to put Captain Clark, Lieutenant Dunkerley and Sergeant Harrison to work, under my direct supervision, on the records and the preparation of preliminary narratives. The First Army had a considerable advantage in being allowed to work for long periods on the records at Com Z.

In any case I wish to take time out and personally prepare one pamphlet on the BRITTANY campaign, for submission to the Army Commander and the Army staff. I cannot wait for others in Paris or Washington to do the job for me, nor do I wish to take the responsibility, in an initial pamphlet, or presenting the work of other individuals, outside this detachment, as a product of this detachment.

I believe that you will not regard this memorandum as evidence of a bilious and hypercritical nature. I think you will understand that it results, not from an ill-regulated glandular flow, but from rather too long a period of concern over what precisely is required of me and my detachment.

Cordially yours,

H.M. COLE,
Major, Ordnance,

APPENDIX C

Office of the Theater Historian

19 December 1944

SUBJECT: Recommendation for Award of Legion of Merit

TO: Adjutant General
       United States Army
       Washington, D.C.

THROUGH: Channels

1. a. It is recommended that Lieutenant Colonel S.L.A. Marshall, 0-102920, GSC, Historical Section, European Theater of Operations, be awarded the Legion of Merit.

b. Lieutenant Colonel S.L.A. Marshall was serving on detached service from Historical Branch, G-2, War Department, at the time of the service for which this award is recommended.

c. Name and address of nearest relative is Mrs. S.L.A. Marshall, 324 Trinity Place, West Palm Beach, Florida.

d. Entered military service from the State of Michigan.

e. Decorations previously awarded: None.

f. The entire service of Lieutenant Colonel S.L.A. Marshall has been honorable since the rendition by him of the service upon which this recommendation is based.

2. The officer recommending this award has personal knowledge of the service upon which this recommendation is based.

3. Lieutenant Colonel S.L.A. Marshall, while a member of the armed forces of the United States, distinguished himself by exceptionally meritorious conduct in the performance of outstanding services.

4. Lieutenant Colonel S.L.A. Marshall became attached to the European Theater of Operations as Deputy Theater Historian in May 1944.

5. Lieutenant Colonel S.L.A. Marshall served as a member of the Historical Branch, G-2, WDGS, from 1 August 1943 to 15 November 1944, when he transferred to Historical Section, ETOUSA. During August, September, and October of 1943, Colonel Marshall researched and wrote a complete and detailed account of the Tokyo raid under General Doolittle's command in May 1942. Because of its classification this account has never been published but it has been widely used and referred to by the General Staff. Lieutenant Colonel S.L.A. Marshall was then sent on temporary duty to the Central Pacific Theater as the first Combat Historian to accompany a military operation. He was with the 27th Division throughout its operation for the capture of Makin Island. He wrote in exhaustive detail a complete account in something less than three months of this operation and received the attached commendation from the Commanding General, 27th Division. This account will shortly be published. Lieutenant Colonel S.L.A. Marshall then accompanied the 7th Division on the Kwajalein operation and wrote the history of that campaign. He was awarded the combat infantryman's badge and was also commended by the Commanding General, 7th Division.

While he was in the Central Pacific preparing these two histories, he developed a highly successful technique of interviewing groups as large as a company. This technique has been extremely important in the reconstruction of confused actions of small units which have hitherto escaped the military historian. Aside from the historical value of this method of research it has a high training and morale value for the units interviewed which has been favorably commented upon by a great number of field commanders.

Upon his return to the United States in April, a description of his methods was published by the Infantry Journal and circulated throughout the Army. Without exception, every commander who received this article expressed his great interest in it and many indicated a desire to have it tried out in their own units. These reactions are on file in the office of the editor of the Infantry Journal. Extracts of Lieutenant Colonel S.L.A. Marshall's Kwajalein history have recently appeared in a book form.

In June 1944 Lieutenant Colonel S.L.A. Marshall was sent on temporary duty in the European Theater. Since that time he has completely and single-handedly written up the Normandy operations of the 82d and 101st Airborne

Divisions. This study is based on the same methods which he developed in the Pacific and runs to well over a hundred thousand words, the length of an ordinary book. In addition, he has cleared up many doubtful points in the history of other phases in this campaign by interviewing units of other divisions, going wherever necessary to companies and platoons actually in contact with the enemy.

As a result of his pioneering, his methods are now in general use by combat historians in all theaters of the war. He has, by his personal example, demonstrated how courage, tact, and enterprise can solve the many problems faced in the collection of historical material on the battlefield where and while it is fresh in men's minds. Lieutenant Colonel S.L.A. Marshall in sixteen months has written the equivalent of five full-length books, material for which has been collected during combat on at least four battlefields. His imagination, resourcefulness and personal example have not only accomplished a prodigious amount of work but have set an inspiring example for all other officers and enlisted men who have followed him as combat historian.

> JOHN M. KEMPER
> Colonel, GSC
> Chief, Hist Br, G-2, WDGS

SELECTED BIBLIOGRAPHY

NOTE ON SOURCES

A large portion of this work derives from Marshall himself, albeit in an indirect manner. While a fair amount of material references General Marshall and his experiences, with the exception of his autobiography, *Bringing Up the Rear,* I encountered no study of him of any depth. Hopefully this work will begin to rectify that situation. A caution must necessarily be added, however. Since there are few published works on Marshall, and since he died prior to this writing, *Bringing Up the Rear* became an invaluable source—invaluable in that it pointed the way when there was often no direction. But—and this is a significant caveat—*Bringing Up the Rear* is an autobiography and was treated as such. All material contained therein was weighed, measured, and double-checked before it was used.

A great deal of data was taken from the S.L.A. Marshall Military History Collection housed at the Library of the University of Texas at El Paso. Military documents, correspondence, manuscripts, and a variety of memorabilia make up this considerable collection. Many thanks go to its curator, Thomas F. Burdett, as well as its chief guardian, Mrs. Cate Marshall, for their assistance and guidance.

Marshall's after-action group interviews were recorded in his field notebooks, of which he claimed to have written 800. Some can be found in the Archives of the Military History Institute at Carlisle Barracks, Pennsylvania, but most are unaccounted for. These are reputed to be in the National Archives or Library of Congress with the rest of the Historical Branch's source documents.

BOOKS BY S.L.A. MARSHALL

MARSHALL, S.L.A., *The American Heritage History of World War I.* New York: American Heritage Publishing, 1964.

_____, *Ambush.* Nashville: The Battery Press, 1983.

_____, *Armies on Wheels.* New York: William Morrow, 1941.

_____, The Armed Forces Officer. U.S. Department of Defense Pamphlet No. 1-20. Washington, D.C.: Government Printing Office, 1975.

_____, *Bastogne: The First Eight Days.* Washington, D.C.: Infantry Journal Press, 1946.

_____, *Battle at Best.* New York: William Morrow, 1963.

_____, *Battles in the Monsoon.* New York: William Morrow, 1967.

_____, *Bird.* New York: Cowles, 1968.

_____, *Blitzkrieg.* Rahway, NJ: Quinn & Boden, 1940.

_____, *Bringing Up the Rear,* ed. Cate Marshall. San Raphael, CA: Presidio Press, 1979.

_____, *Crimsoned Prairie.* New York: Scribner's, 1972.

_____, *The Fields of Bamboo.* New York: Dial Press, 1971. Published in 1982 as *Vietnam: Three Battles.*

_____, *Island Victory.* Washington, D.C.: Zenger Publishing, 1982.

_____, *Lessons Learned: Vietnam Primer.* Washington, D.C.: Department of the Army Pamphlet 525-2, 1967.

_____, *Men Against Fire.* Gloucester, MS.: Peter Smith, 1978.

_____, *The Military History of the Korean War.* New York: F. Watts, 1963.

_____, *Night Drop.* Nashville: Battery Press, 1983.

_____, *The Officer as a Leader.* Harrisburg, PA: Stackpole, 1966. Originally published as Department of Defense Pamphlet 1-20, 1950.

_____, *The Officer as a Leader.* Harrisburg, PA: Stackpole, 1966. Originally published as Department of Defense Pamphlet 1-20, 1950.

_____, *Pork Chop Hill.* New York: William Morrow, 1956.

_____, *The River and the Gauntlet.* Alexandria, VA: Time-Life Books, 1982.

_____, *Sinai Victory.* New York: William Morrow, 1958.

_____, *The Soldier's Load and the Mobility of a Nation.* Quantico, VA: The Marine Corps Association, January 1980.

_____, *Swift Sword.* New York: American Heritage, 1967.

_____, *Vietnam: Three Battles.* New York: Da Capo Press, 1982.

_____, *West to Cambodia.* New York: Cowles, 1968.

OTHER SOURCES

A. UNPUBLISHED SOURCES

l. Letters, Memoranda, Military Orders

S.L.A. Marshall Military History Collection, University of Texas at El Paso, El Paso, Texas.

United States Army Military History Institute Archives, Carlisle Barracks, Pennsylvania.

2. Correspondence Concerning S.L.A. Marshall

Calahan, J.E., Lieutenant Colonel, USA, retired.

Cavazos, Richard E., General, USA.

Clark, Mark W., General, USA, retired.

Clarke, Bruce C., General, USA, retired.

Cole, Hugh M.

Collins, Arthur S., Jr., Lieutenant General, USA, retired.

Desobry, William R., Lieutenant General, USA, retired.

DePuy, William E., General, USA, retired.

Ewell, Julian J., Lieutenant Colonel, USA.

Fairchild, Robert P., Lieutenant Colonel, USA.

Gavin, James M., Lieutenant General, USA, retired.

Gray, David H., Major General, USA, retired.

Griess, Thomas E., Brigadier General, USA, retired.

Hammond, James W., Jr., Colonel, USMC, retired.

Harkins, Paul D., General, USA, retired.

Harper, Joseph H., Major General, USA, retired.
Hillman, Rolfe L., Jr., Colonel, USA, retired.
Horner, Charles T., Jr., Major General, USA, retired.
Howze, Hamilton H., General, USA, retired.
Irish, Hugh H., Colonel, USMC, retired.
Kinnard, Harry W.O., Lieutenant General, USA, retired.
Leckie, Robert.
Lopez, Joe, Sergeant Major, USA.
McCaffrey, William J., Lieutenant General, USA, retired.
Meyer, Edward C., General, USA, retired.
Newman, Aubrey S., Major General, USA, retired.
Palmer, Bruce, General, USA, retired.
Parker, Edward M., Colonel, USA, retired.
Pogue, Forrest C.
Spiller, Roger.
Starry, Donn A., General, USA, retired.
Stilwell, Rilchard G., General, USA, retired.
Taylor, Maxwell D., General, USA, retired.
Trudeau, Arthur S., Lieutenant General, USA, retired.
Westmoreland, William C., General, USA, retired.
Westover, John.

3. Interviews
a. Personal
Belenke, Gregory, M.D., Lieutenant Colonel, USA.
Collins, Arthur S., Lieutenant General, USA, retired.
Ewell, Julian J., Major General, USA, retired.
Marshall, Mrs. S.L.A.
McCaffrey, William J., Lieutenant General, USA, retired.
Trudeau, Arthur G., Lieutenant General, USA, retired.

b. Telephone
Belenke, Gregory M.D., Lieutenant Colonel, USA.
Cirillo, Roger, Major, USA.

Doyle, David, General, USA.

Finke, Detmar.

Frasche, Louis D.F., Colonel, USA.

Howard, Michael.

Kant, Jean.

Janowitz, Morris.

Kinnard, Harry W.O., Lieutenant General, USA, retired.

Wells, Jerry L., Sergeant First Class, USA.

B. PUBLISHED SOURCES

BAKER, ROBERT A., et al., "Development of Proficiency Tests for Basic Combat and Light Infantry Training." Washington, D.C.: George Washington University, Human Resources Research Office, Report No. TR-19, July 1955.

BROWN, FRANK L., "Pass on that Combat Lore." *Army,* September 1966.

BULFINCH, THOMAS, *Bulfinch's Mythology: The Age of Fable.* Garden City, NJ: Doubleday, 1968.

CLARK, RODNEY A., "Leadership in Rifle Squads on the Korean Front Line." Washington, D.C.: George Washington University, Human Resources Research Office, Report No. TR-21, September 1955.

COLEMAN, J.D., "Ego Interferes with Marshall Memoirs." *Soldier of Fortune,* April 1981.

COLLINS, ARTHUR S., JR., *Common Sense Training.* San Raphael, CA: Presidio Press, 1978.

CONN, STETSON, "Historical Work in the United States Army: 1862-1954." Washington, D.C.: U.S. Center of Military History, 1980.

CLAUSEWITZ, CARL VON, *On War,* ed./trans. Michael Howard and Peter Paret. Princeton: Princeton University Press, 1976.

DANIELS, FARRINGTON, JR., *The Energy Cost of Carrying Three Load Distributions on a Treadmill.* Natick, MA: Quartermaster Research Laboratory, Environmental Research Branch, Quartermaster Research and Development Command, Report No. 461, November 1955.

_____, *Physiology of Load Carrying I.* Natick, MA: Quartermaster Research Laboratory, Environmental Research Branch, Quartermaster Research and Development Command, Report No. 203, March 1953.

DAVIDSON, BILL, "Why Our Combat Soldiers Fail to Shoot." *Collier's,* November 8, 1952.

DEUTSCH, JOHANN N., "A Slam for Marshall." *Army Times,* January 29, 1963.

DOUGHTY, ROBERT A., *The Evolution of U.S. Army Tactical Doctrine, 1946-76.* Fort Leavenworth, KS: Combat Studies Institute, U.S. Army Command and General Staff College, August 1979.

DU PICQ, ARDANT, *Battle Studies.* trans. Colonel John N. Greely and Major Robert C. Cotton, Harrisonburg, PA: The Military Service Publishing Company, 1946.

EGBERT, ROBERT L., et al., *Fighters: An Analysis of Combat Fighters and Non-Fighters.* Washington, D.C.: George Washington University, Human Resources Research Office, Report No. TR-44, December 1957.

ELLIS, JOHN, *The Sharp End.* New York: Scribner's, 1980.

GREENFIELD, KENT R., *The Historian and the Army.* New Brunswick, NJ: Rutgers University Press, 1954.

GUILMARTIN, JOHN F., JR., "Military Experience, the Military Historian, and the Reality of Battle." Paper presented at the Shelley Cullom Davis Center for Historical Studies, Princeton University, October 8, 1982.

HACKWORTH, DAVID., "Battle Analysis." *Army,* May/June 1967.

HAMMES, JOHN A., et al., *Trainfire II: A New Course in Basic Technique of Fire and Squad Tactics.* Washington, D.C.: George Washington University, Human Resources Research Office, Report No. TR-41, July 1957.

HAVRON, M. DEAN, et al., *Tactical Training of the Infantry Rifle Squad.* Washington, D.C.: George Washington University, Human Resources Research Office, Technical Report No. 18, June 1955.

HORNER, THOMAS A., "Killers, Fillers, and Fodder." *Parameters,* September 1982.

KEEGAN, JOHN, "Battle and the Historian." *International Security,* Winter 1978-79.

_____, *The Face of Battle.* New York: Viking Press, 1976.

LAFFARGUE, ANDRE, *The Attack in Trench Warfare.* Washington, D.C.: The United States Infantry Association, 1916.

LOTHIAN, N.V., *The Load Carried by the Soldier.* Army School of Hygiene, Army Hygiene Advisory Committee, Report No. 1. London: John Dale, 1918.

MARSHALL, S.L.A., "CCF in the Attack." Part I, Staff Memorandum ORO-S-26, EUSAK, January 5, 1951.

_____, "CCF in the Attack." Part II, Staff Memorandum ORO-S-34, EUSAK, January 27, 1951.

_____, "CCF Tactics in the Envelopment of a Column." Staff Memorandum ORO-S-25, EUSAK, December 20, 1950.

_____, "Commentary on Infantry Operations and Weapons Usage in Korea; Winter of 1950-51." The Johns Hopkins University, Operations Research Office, Report No. ORO-R-13, October 27, 1951.

_____, "Notes on CCF Area Targets Based on CCF Tactics." Staff Memorandum ORO-S-4, EUSAK, January 2, 1951.

_____, "Notes on Chinese Company Tactics." The Johns Hopkins University, Operations Research Office Report No. ORO-S-41, EUSAK, December 16, 1950.

_____, "Notes on Infantry Tactics in Korea." The Johns Hopkins University, Operations Research Office, Report No. ORO-T-7, EUSAK, 1951.

_____, "Notes on Urban Warfare." Aberdeen Proving Ground, MD: U.S. Army Materiel Systems Agency, 1973.

_____, "On Being Commissioned: The Commissioning Day Address at the University of Virginia, Charlottesville, Virginia," June 7, 1969.

_____, "Operation Punch and the Capture of Hill 440." The Johns Hopkins University, Operations Research Office, Report No. ORO-T-190, 1952.

_____, "Speaking of Team Play," *Army*, October 1957.

MATTHEWS, RICHARD T., "The Load of the Individual Soldier." *Combat Forces Journal*, October 1952.

MCFANN, HOWARD H., et al., "Trainfire I: A New Course in Basic Rifle Marksmanship." Washington, D.C.: George Washington University, Human Resources Research Office, Report No. TR-22, October 1955.

MEYER, EDWARD C., "Time of Transition: A Focus on Quality." *Army*, October 1982.

NEWMAN, AUBREY S., *Follow Me: The Human Element in Leadership*. San Raphael, CA: Presidio Press, 1981.

_____, "Think Time is Vital in Command." *Army*, August 1982.

PARKER, EDWARD M.,"Trial by Combat." *Combat Forces Journal*, May 1951.

POGUE, FORREST C., *George C. Marshall: Education of a General.* Vol. I. New York: Viking Press, 1968.

RIDGWAY, MATTHEW B., *The Korean War.* Garden City, NJ: Doubleday, 1967.

SHILS, EDWARD A., and MORRIS JANOWITZ, "Cohesion and Disintegration in the Wehrmacht in World War II." *Public Opinion Quarterly*, Summer 1948.

SHRIVER, EDGAR L., et al., "Realtrain: A New Method for Tactical Training of Small Units." Kinton, Inc., Technical Report No. S-4, December 1975.

SPILLER, ROGER J., "The Marshall-Liddell Hart Correspondence." *Newsletter of the S.L.A. Marshall Military History Collection,* January 1984.

_____, "S.L.A. Marshall at Leavenworth." Fort Leavenworth, KS: U.S. Army Command and General Staff College, 1980.

STANDISH, ANTHONY, "Crisis in Courage." *Combat Forces Journal,* April 1952.

STOUFFER, SAMUEL A., *The American Soldier: Combat and its Aftermath.* Princeton: Princeton University Press, 1949.

(United States, Army General School), *Leadership for the Company Officer.* Army General School Special Text Number 1, Revised. Fort Riley, KS: (Army General School), 1950.

WILLIAMS, PEYTON R., JR., "The Combat Stress Threat," Walter Reed Army Institute of Research, Summer 1983.

WILLIAMS, RICHARD HAYS, ed., "Human Factors in Military Operations." Washington, D.C.: Johns Hopkins University, Operations Research Office, Report No. ORO-T-259, January 1954.

YAHRAES, HERBERT, "The Mysterious Mission of ORO." *Saturday Evening Post,* February 23, 1952.

INDEX